To Rev. J. C. Stewart,

With best Wishes,

- Roseleen Milne -

1949.

The Major's Lady

By the same author

BORROWED PLUMES

The Major's Lady

by

Roseleen Milne

HODDER AND STOUGHTON
LONDON SYDNEY AUCKLAND TORONTO

British Library Cataloguing in Publication Data
Milne, Roseleen
    The major's lady.
    I. Title
    823'.9'15   PR6063.1379M/

ISBN 0 340 24082 2

To my father and mother

1

THE TWO JUNIOR officers lingering over luncheon in the tap-room of the Rose and Crown at Tewin were evidently in no haste to depart but the landlord's anxiety for the poached game hidden in a cupboard next to the hearth was dispelled upon recognising in the blond major the younger son of Lady Auden, who before her marriage to the viscount had been one of the beautiful Hurst sisters from Linkdown, a family long established in Hertfordshire and the foremost in the neighbourhood.

Both gentlemen were in their late twenties and wore the blue coat of the Light Cavalry, but the furred and braided pelisse slung over the left shoulder denoted the splendour of a hussar regiment. The landlord, well versed in the history pertaining to one of the pair, felt liberally disposed to repeat it in confidence to the cook in the kitchens beyond.

To be sure, young Master Christopher had been a roaring boy from his cradle upwards. He had narrowly escaped expulsion from Eton for Heaven knows what misbegotten sins, and had remained just eleven months at Oxford before descending on town to acquire such appalling familiarity with all matters he ought not, that his crowning romp with a high-born lady of dubious reputation delivered him swiftly into the service of His Most Gracious Majesty King George.

The pretty dasher in question had been possessed of wit, notoriety and an irate husband — which combination decided a scandalised Lady Auden that her offspring's energies might more suitably be directed in laying siege to the armies of Bonaparte.

Thus young Fane found himself gazetted firmly into the 18th Hussars.

"What's this cousin of yours like, Kit? A comely lass, is she?"

Major Fane appeared wholly astonished by the question.

"*Dindie*? She's only a baby!"

James Drummond set down his fork and leaned back against the curved high-back settle. "You said the other day that Miss Smith was sixteen years old," he accused.

"Well, she *is*! I was eleven and a bit when she was born. That makes her . . . lord, almost seventeen."

Kit Fane crossed his pantalooned limbs and studied the tassel dangling from the V-shaped front of one Hessian boot.

"Dorinda is a taking little thing. Not a looker — I mean, she's nowhere in my sister Kate's class. Her nose turns up rather, and she has brownish hair." His expression softened. "Dindie's my best girl. Always was."

The young captain cocked him a dubious eyebrow.

"Presumably she comes somewhere in your battle honours between Mrs Dolly Vere-Parker and yon sparky wee besom with the generous super-structure. The one you were devouring at Rochester Assembly."

"James," chided his friend, with mock severity. "You have studied my sieges of the muslin brigade over seven glorious years. Oh, you may look disapproving but in all fairness I was devouring only the lady's hand — in any event, you were bent upon fixing your interest with Miss Amabel Wilmot until of late."

"I had as lief not discuss Miss Amabel!" declared Captain Drummond, with quiet menace.

Kit inwardly cursed his own tactlessness. He had assumed Jamie to be over the Wilmot business but the wounds were evidently still raw. An awkward pause ensued then Kit demanded, with mock accusation, "What the deuce are you about, asking after my cousin? I've not set eyes on Dindie in four years!"

James Drummond smiled and pushed aside his empty plate. A dark brooding fellow, he was a year older than Kit and his soft, pronounced accent stamped him as hailing from north of the border.

"Yon's the grandest cured ham I've tasted in a twelvemonth," he remarked in round satisfaction. "But if you intend to break our journey we ought to be spurring on. How far is it to Linkdown?"

"Oh, my cousin don't live there! Grandfather Hurst has never acknowledged her existence. It — it's an affair of some delicacy." Kit looked a shade embarrassed. "I'll explain on the way. No — allow me to settle the reckoning, Jamie," he added quickly, seeing his friend signal to the landlord. "Your pockets are gutted and my conscience still pricks over this promotion business."

"As to that! You've earned General Moore's favour and you'll make him a first class aide-de-camp." Jamie grimaced, adding thoughtfully, "I only hope I can step into your shoes with the same confidence. You have turned C Troop into a crack outfit — the men are bound to compare me unfavourably."

"By rights you should have had a company command long before now. It's no disgrace that the regulation price has always been above your touch. Why, the entire regiment is delighted for you from Colonel Stewart down."

A grin split Jamie's countenance. "I'll wager Dan Flannigan would disagree — yon shilpit wee worm has been a thorn in my side since the day he joined."

Kit set his furred hussar cap at a dashing angle and chuckled. "You have at least the solace of knowing he hates my insides several degrees more than he does yours! Go bespeak a couple of horses from the ostler. I'll rejoin you outside in a tick."

Some fifteen minutes later they were cantering down a rutted country lane hedged by woodbine and wild grasses. The hot July sun burned their faces, provoking a good-natured curse; the summer of 1808 seemed bent upon surpassing all other years in thundery stickiness. A few miles distant brought them to the first scattered cottages of the village of Dean. Kit indicated an unpretentious brick house standing half-hidden by trees some way off the road. Its walls were hung with ivy and the modest garden fenced in by a wooden paling.

"That is where my cousin lives," he remarked soberly.

As they trotted over the fields towards the house, James Drummond learned something of this young relative whose Mama, youngest of the Hurst sisters, had so forgotten herself as to elope with a penniless country doctor by the name of Smith.

"Grandfather never forgave Aunt Corinne. The entire family closed ranks against her. Slur on the Hurst honour and such like fustian!" The bronzed good looks darkened with anger. "I never could comprehend bigotry of that sort. Mother neither, thank Heaven! She did her utmost to make life easier for 'em, especially after Dindie was born. Poor as church mice, you see, and too fiercely proud to ask for assistance."

"There's spunk. It's not every woman that's game to fling her cap over a windmill for love."

The remark held an undeniable bitterness. Not for the first time did Kit wish he might deliver a few choice words to Amabel Wilmot. Jamie was deucedly cut up and it was all the more hard because until this affair he had never shown much interest in the petticoat line. But the girl had refused him and would be riveted to five thousand a year come December. There was not much one could say to soften the blow.

"Yes, Aunt Corinne had guts," he said at last. "Dindie, too. She was devoted to her Papa. It prostrated her fearfully when he died. I liked him, you know. He was well read and would have put many a so-called gentleman to shame."

Reining his animal to a halt he surveyed the modest dwelling with an air of curiosity. "I've not set foot here since my aunt remarried. That is another tragedy," he added, frowning. "Aunt Corinne died in childbed just three months ago."

Jamie whistled softly. "So your cousin is now orphaned — apart from the step-father?"

Chris nodded. "She has a companion, former abigail to my aunt. Stout old thing, Miss Fisher. And I believe Harker, the step-father, has installed his sister in the house. Poor little chicken," he added, to himself. "I ought to have remained in closer touch."

A peculiar air of lifelessness pervaded the exterior of the house. No sign of activity, no welcoming bark from the spaniels which had once been a feature of the place, no merry brown eyes watching eagerly from the window. It was distinctly odd, thought Kit. Dindie's letter had been particularly urgent and she must know that he would come.

They dismounted before the gate and Kit went forward to lift the brass knocker. Just then the sash of a ground-floor window was flung upwards and an elderly female in mittens and cap hung over the sill and gesticulated with one bony finger pressed to her lips.

Striding to the window Kit bent down to communicate with the agitated spinster. "I say, Fish old thing, where is my favourite cousin? I'm dashed if I was able to make sense of that scribble she sent. What the blazes is afoot?"

Miss Fisher wrung her mittened hands distractedly.

"Oh, sir, I'm that relieved to see you! Miss Dorinda is waiting in the copse. Been on the listen for you this hour past, she has. But go now before himself returns! Took Miss Harker to the village in the gig not ten minutes since. Not but that she's capable of using Shank's mare like other folks. Detestable creature!"

"Why, Fish . . . it's unlike you to speak ill of anyone."

"It's the way she treats my poor, darling Miss Dorinda, sir. Taken over she has, cool as you please — and making free with the trinkets left by the mistress. If you but knew the goings on it would tear your heart out. And how Miss Dorinda is to fare once I go . . ." She searched for a handkerchief and wiped at her eyes. "The good Lord knows what's to become of her."

"*You*, Fish — leaving here? But that's out of the question! Miss Dindie needs you — why, you can't go."

The spinster blew her nose, injured feeling imprinted on her face. "I'm not going out of choice, sir. Friday by ten sharpish. No further use for my services."

"Miss Dindie has asked you to leave?"

11

"Bless you, no — it's him as has usurped the master's place. But there, you must make haste — if he should return and find your horses outside Miss Dorinda will be denied leave to talk private."

"We shall see about that!" declared Kit, grimly.

Miss Fisher's intelligence both angered and disturbed him. That his young cousin should be bullied and treated as a mere lodger, that some unknown harpy could be so devoid of compassion as to flaunt his aunt's possessions before Dindie's eyes . . . Rage possessed him. Signalling to Jamie he remounted and together they rode swiftly back the way they had come, making for the dark clump of trees that was the copse.

They tethered their horses to a gnarled oak and proceeded on foot. The dry earth made a noiseless carpet as they pushed deeper into the undergrowth. Without warning a clearing emerged dappled by thin sunlight.

A girl stood alone, absorbed in the antics of a grey squirrel in the branches above. It was only when Kit softly called her name that she started, staring uncomprehendingly, then with a little cry ran towards him.

"*Kit* . . . you *have* come! Oh, I knew you would."

The major caught his cousin about the waist and swung her off the ground as one might a child. Laughing she flung her arms about his neck, her eyes alight with the joy of reunion. Then suddenly shy she wriggled free, rubbing her cheek where the hard silver lace of his uniform had brushed her skin, and glanced uncertainly towards Captain Drummond who had hung back, not wishing to intrude.

"Dindie, I want you to meet James Drummond, the finest comrade-in-arms a fellow ever had. Jamie, come pay your respects. I warn you, Dindie, this Scots giant has plagued me with all manner of quizzing concerning you since we left Rochester barracks."

Jamie coloured self-consciously and stepped forward. He had expected to meet a school-room miss, all blushes and bread-and-butter, but although Miss Smith was indeed a very young lady her

12

figure was already pleasingly formed. She wore a stuff gown buttoned closely to her throat and her hair, which she still wore in ringlets about her shoulders, was secured by a mourning ribbon.

Everything about her was freshly youthful — the clear skin of her cheeks and forehead, the fluffy hairs that sprouted at her hairline, the frank innocence in the brown eyes which smiled shyly back at him as she placed her hand in his. And when she laughed, as presently she did by dint of her cousin's teasing, James Drummond decided that however lowly her charms might rate with his friend little Miss Smith was entirely captivating.

Not that she was by any means diminutive, for the top of her head reached almost level with her cousin's shoulder and her carriage was good. It was also clear from the hasty scrubbing at her eyes with the back of one hand that she had been weeping.

"Why, Dindie — you are grown up of a sudden!" Kit held her a little from him to inspect her inches. "It seems only yesterday that you were a puny seven-year-old fetching balls for me at cricket. Do you realise, Jamie — "

"Kit." Dindie spoke with an air of breathless insistence. "I must talk with you . . ." Beseechingly she turned to his companion. "If you please, sir — "

"I'll just stretch my legs for a bit." The young captain flashed her an understanding smile and strode off through the trees.

"Fish mentioned some unpleasantness." Kit led his cousin to a tree-stump and sat himself next her. "Care to tell me about it?"

Dindie remained silent, eyes downcast as though summoning courage to speak. "You — you *do* like me, Kit? I mean, I'm not a nuisance or — or anything?"

"I should think not!" He drew her warmly towards him, ruffling her hair. "I told Jamie you were my best girl and so you are."

She looked up then, twisting round to face him, her eyes big with hope. "Then . . . Kit, will you — oh, *please* will you take me with you when you go?"

Seeing his start of incredulity she rushed on, nervously, "I

13

cannot remain here — indeed I cannot! You can have no notion how wretched it has been since M-Mama . . ."

A great sob carried away the remainder of her words and she dissolved into tears. Awkwardly Major Fane drew his cousin close, soothing her gently until she lay quietly against his shoulder. Gradually it all emerged. The shock of her Mama's remarriage, the harsh, bullish disciplinarian who had taken her father's place and who so cowed her pretty Mama that she was afraid to remonstrate. The animosity, the frequent explosions of violence when her step-father took more wine than he ought, the dismay of finding Mama with child when the entire village sorrowfully predicted her to be past the age of an untroubled lying-in.

"I could not believe she was dead, not at first." Dindie stared down at her entwined fingers. "They placed the baby in her arms, you know, before — before nailing the coffin. His tiny face was quite blue, Kit. But Mama . . . Mama looked so peaceful lying there I was almost glad — for I knew she was beyond whatever grief *he* may have caused!" The young face tensed fiercely." Why, oh why did she choose to accept him?"

"To ensure security for you both, Dindie," reasoned Kit, firmly. "Look, tell me more of this Harker character."

Haltingly Dindie complied. Her step-father was a man of some substance with a business in St. Albans. It was whispered that his own sire had been a common wheelwright and that the doctor's widow was sought solely on account of her connections with the wealthy Hursts of Linkdown.

"A Cit," declared Kit, scornfully. "I suspected as much. In trade," he added, seeing her brows wrinkle.

"You mean not a proper gentleman? Indeed no, although he was vastly attentive at the first." She scraped at the soft ferns with one toecap, saying fiercely, "Soon after the wedding-day he began to upbraid Mama, storming at her to attempt a reconciliation with Grandfather Hurst. I — I know that he struck her more than once although she refused to admit of it."

Dindie swallowed and dropped her gaze. "He scares me, Kit. I

14

said nothing to Fish at the time but . . ." Her voice faltered. "When he is in his cups my step-father becomes obnoxiously familiar. He . . . he has attempted to k-kiss me on two occasions of late. And when Fish leaves I — "

"He has dared to molest you?" Chris swore softly. His fingers tightened on her wrist. He felt the racing of her pulse and realised the effort which the admission had wrung from her. She turned away flushing but he cupped her chin firmly round, his emotions so a-boil that only with difficulty could he contain his wrath. Fleetingly he wondered if she truly understood the reason behind his unease. Either way he must not frighten her. Carefully he demanded, "Dindie, is what you have confided the whole? You have left nothing out? I must and shall know!"

Dindie closed her eyes tightly then raising her face to meet his, said shakily, "On Sunday last — just after midnight — someone tried the door to my bedchamber. Truly, Kit, I did not imagine it!" Her lips pressed fiercely together. "I know it could only have been him. His step is unmistakable and he was breathing heavily and muttering as he always does when foxed. I was too scared to move . . . I listened and listened, long after the footsteps had died away. I — I did not dare to sleep. When I was certain he had gone I unbolted the door and ran to waken Fish."

"Thank God you had the good sense to lock your door." Grim-faced, Kit swung her to her feet. "You shall not remain another day under his so-called protection! Mama is presently with Kate at Fairlands. They will make you more than welcome."

"Oh . . . I had much sooner not." Dindie's face fell. "You must know how conscious Mr Farriday is of Kate being related to me. I should only be the means of causing conflict between them. Besides . . . "

Besides, she thought with a sinking heart, Kate will not thank you for foisting me upon her. Kit and his sister were different as April and December. Kate had always been spoilt and wilful, possessing even in childhood an awareness of her own beauty. She had deplored rough games, preferring to prink before the glass and making little attempt to hide the fact that she despised the countrified little cousin who came to pass the summer months and who tried so hard to emulate her in accomplishments.

Kate's was a startling prettiness, the sort that caused gentlemen to stare. Her skin was pink and white, her curls golden, her demeanour ladylike, all in all serving to underline Dindie's inadequacies. Dindie was three years younger, a dreamy child, all coltish arms and legs. She easily outshone Kate at lessons but had early made the discovery that a quick mind counted for little against birth and beauty.

In high summer Dindie's sallow complexion would turn a healthy golden-brown, 'like a gypsy child', as Kate scornfully remarked. Kate knew how to hurt. As they grew older a compatibility had formed between them but Dindie sensed that Kate and she would never become close. And as Kate developed in beauty Dindie resigned herself to making the most of her own unexceptional looks. She had pretty teeth and her eyes were long-lashed but no matter how Fish might describe her locks as 'dark-fair' Dindie knew her hair for what it was — mouse brown.

"No," she decided, firmly. "I mean to go to London. An advertisement in the *Gazette* should answer. I believe I might do very well as a governess."

"A — a governess! You, Dindie?" Kit was aghast, torn between horror and a strong desire to laugh. "Why, you're no more than a child yourself. No, no," he added hastily, seeing her crestfallen expression, "there must be no governesses in our family." He studied her keenly. "Why will you not go to Kate?"

"You know why . . ." She struggled for words. "Mr Farriday considers me a pauper. Indeed he does, so you need not pretend! And I shan't go to Cousin George neither, for he never liked me."

As Kit had been about to nominate that very suggestion her vehemence left him nonplussed. Not that he blamed her. Since his elder brother had inherited the title he was grown even more of a prig than before. Now that he was also the father of a hopeful family the new viscount showed every sign of developing into a preaching, humourless snob. He was hardly likely to welcome an outcast cousin into his rarified circle.

As though reading his thoughts, Dindie's chin lifted proudly. "I have no need of anyone's charity. If you will only take me as far as town, Kit, I promise to prevail on you no further."

Her independent hauteur caused him to turn away to hide a smile. She was trying so hard to appear grown up and indeed he had to own she was no longer the child of his remembrance. Surreptitiously he glanced at her thrusting young breasts, the soft pout of her lips. No, indeed. His duckling was fairly emerging into womanhood.

Plucking at a leaf he asked, "What about Fish? Where does she go?"

"She means to settle with her sister in Chelsea. But I could not impose upon them, Kit," she added, horrified. "Why, their savings must barely suffice for their own needs."

"Then what in the world are we to do with you, Dindie?" Kit ran a finger inside the white collar of his tunic. "Depend upon it, I shall not deposit you in town to fend for yourself so you may promptly discard the idea."

Dindie regarded him shyly. "Might I not return with you to barracks? Only until I find a lodging in Rochester, of course," she added hastily, turning pink. "My music has improved excessively, Kit. I am certain of obtaining a post as instruct — "

"Dindie, listen to me!" Kit caught at her hands. "Within the week I'm due to sail for Portugal with General Moore. The entire army is under orders. I cannot take you to Rochester or — or anywhere else for that matter."

"To Portugal?" she whispered. "I . . . I see."

She fell silent, overcome by the unexpectedness of his news. Kit slipped an arm about her shoulder, cursing himself for his brusqueness. "You do understand, Dindie? I must be in town within two days to complete my preparations."

A twig breaking underfoot caused him to glance up. "Jamie, come help us out. We are in no end of a fangle here."

Captain Drummond listened whilst the situation was outlined. "I know fine it's out of the question," he said at length. "But the only solution I see is to bring the lass along."

Dindie squealed her delight. "Oh, *do* say yes, Kit! I should strive to make myself useful. I know how to scrape lint and measure a draught correctly — Papa showed me how." She clung imploringly to his hand. "I — I had liefer go with you than with anyone!"

"Dindie, the thing is impossible." Gently Kit disengaged her fingers. Her earnestness both touched and alarmed him. This belief in his powers was so unshakeable, her dependence on him so absolute.

It had always been so, he reflected, recalling the thin, brown child who had trailed after him in summers past, loyally digging worms for his fishing or panting after his long strides on country rambles. When she chanced to scrape her knee or fall in the mill-stream it was to him she had come for comfort. Now she was alone in the world, in need of his protection as never before and certain as ever of its being hers.

But how am I to comply this time? argued Kit. He was inordinately fond of Dindie, he felt responsible for her, he would not fail her were it in his power but there was no way he could take her to Portugal.

All this he endeavoured to explain as gently as he knew how. "As though I should sanction any such ploy. An army on the march is no place for you, coz."

"But women *do* accompany the troops — you told me so in your letters!"

"The women you describe, Miss Smith, are what we call camp followers." Jamie cleared his throat in embarrassment. "Women who — well, not fitting companions for a lady such as yourself."

"But some army wives follow the drum, surely? There is one — I forget her name — who was wounded last year in the Buenos Aires campaign. You remember, Kit — her husband was a sergeant in the Rifles! Why, you devoted a full crossed sheet to the incident."

18

"To be sure, there are always wives ready to go with their men. And naturally, officers are entitled to bring their ladies — "

Jamie paused. Major Fane was staring fixedly at him, looking, as his captain later revealed, like Lot's wife when the ossifying set in.

"By Heaven, so they do." A peculiar expression lingered about the major's grey eyes. Looking down into his cousin's bewildered upturned face, Kit said quietly, "Well, Dindie? Are you willing to run in double harness?"

"Do . . . do what, Kit?" she stammered.

"Why, *marry* me, what else!" Covering her hands he held them in a warm clasp. "It will solve everything! Harker will no longer have a claim on you and I need not leave you behind." He pulled her to her feet, aglow with purpose. "We shall obtain a special licence in town — and I recommend we delay your flight until dawn. We should be all too readily overtaken if we leave now. Why, Dindie . . . don't you care for the prospect? I thought . . . "

Dindie's eyes were misted so that she could scarcely see. How could he suspect that she had cherished the impossibility of this in her heart for as long as she could remember? Since the age of five when she had first become aware of her tall Cousin Kit he had dominated her childish dreams. Kit had been her hero, her Launcelot in shining armour — and now he was asking her to be his wife.

Dindie's knees were trembling and if Kit had not been supporting her she would in all probability have fallen. She wanted to slip her arms about his neck, to thank him for this unspeakable joy but shyness forestalled her. In a halting whisper she heard herself stammer formally, "If you think I shall not be a burden I should like it of all things."

2

"You're glaikit, man! One canna take a wife simply from a sense of obligation!" Jamie, lapsing in the heat of the argument into his native idiom, was proving unusually passionate. "It — it's downright immoral."

He glared across the sparsely furnished bedchamber to where the major stood unheeding before the glass, wrestling with a comb. Kit's hair was cropped rakishly forwards *au coups de vent* after the latest craze, but the blond wisps refused to lie flat with the careless elegance demanded and he abhorred the use of pomatum.

"Damn!" Straightening, he fixed his mentor with an exasperated grin. "Allow me to remind you it's Dindie I'm to wed, not you! And I'm happy as a grig at the prospect, so you may cease behaving like the voice of Doom."

Jamie flushed deeply. "See here, Kit," he coaxed. "I've nothing against your cousin. She's a fine lass. But marriage is a serious undertaking. A man doesna choose a bride as he might a — a new razor!"

"And a fellow's friend ought not to go on at him like an old woman once the choice is made! Lord knows you've been contriving for years to get me under starter's orders. In fact," added Kit, slyly, "I suspect you are jealous. Confess it, you dog. You fancy Dindie yourself."

"Away, you glib-gabbit rascal." James Drummond delivered his friend's ribs an embarrassed prod. "If you are seriously bent upon this folly I wish you joy — you know I do. I simply feel you are blinding yourself to the consequences."

"The thing is beyond second thought," countered Kit firmly. "Dindie and I shall rub along smart as snuff."

"Heaven help you when Colonel Stewart finds out," retorted Jamie, ever practical. "And what about Sir John Moore? You know fine it's frowned on for junior officers to get sewn up. I suppose you mean to go ahead without his authority?"

"I must — there's no time to go by the book."

Kit shrugged on his frogged dolman jacket with an air of defiance. He knew this affair must land him in hot water with his new chief. There was an unwritten law that company fry should be at least thirty before taking the plunge. Well, Dindie could not wait that long. He must simply get it in the neck.

Jamie regarded him in silence. In being appointed to Sir John's personal staff Kit had been accorded the highest honour of his military career. Moore was the soldiers' idol, the first general of the British Army and the most humane commander of his time. His approbation could lift flagging courage, his chilling contempt was more stingingly effective with wrongdoers than any lash. Did Kit really intend to blight the threshold of such sought-after promotion by this flagrant daring?

It was not merely a case of thumbing the nose at the rule-book. Arranging for a special licence would mean a delay calculated to destroy Kit's vital time schedule. A fine start this would prove, missing his ship at Portsmouth and arriving at headquarters with a wife in tow! But with Kit in so belligerent a humour argument was useless.

"Have you thought about Harker?" demanded Jamie. "If that Philistine tumbles your intentions there's no saying how he may react. Did you hear his crust when you introduced me?" His good-natured countenance darkened angrily. " 'Another bloody Scotchman' indeed! Has he never heard how the Black Watch destroyed an entire French column at Alexandria, or that it was General Moore himself that led them? And if he makes one more sneering remark about Moore having been passed over — "

Kit nodded, tight-lipped. Military circles had been shaken by the *Morning Post* announcement. The general's blunt honesty and incorruptibility had made him many enemies in high places, particularly in the Tory Cabinet of Lord Portland, but since his recent recall from Sweden, where he had been forced to negotiate a diplomatic tightrope with the mad and despotic King Gustavus, no one doubted that Sir John would be given the command-in-chief of the Expeditionary Force now mobilising to drive the French from the Peninsula. There could be no question of anyone else — his professionalism, his unrivalled standing throughout the Army demanded it.

And yet, in black and white the newspaper headlines screamed out the vengeful snub. The new commander was to be the aged Sir Hew Dalrymple, an amiable veteran and crony of the Duke of York, whose last shot in anger had been fired all of fourteen years ago.

"And to think they have dragged old Harry Burrard out of retirement to act as second! Good God, Jamie, he's pushing seventy-three! It — it's deliberate treachery."

"The two auld bumblers must be as shocked as anybody," remarked Jamie drily, as they went downstairs to dinner. "If the Horse Guards were bent upon humiliating Moore it's a wonder they didn't fix on Wellesley, instead of allowing him to sail. He's their man — and a Tory to boot. I suppose they didn't dare."

"The Horse Guards would have given the command to the Deuce rather than let Sir John have it," muttered Kit grimly. "Oh, confound 'em. I'm hungry."

The meal which followed was a cheese-paring affair but it progressed without incident although the Harkers were clearly suspicious of their unlooked-for guests. Miss Harker in particular asked a great many searching questions of Major Fane. Jervis Harker, a surly ox of a man, shovelled down his food in noisy grunts, preferring to observe matters from under his black brows. Jamie noticed how frequently his eyes settled upon Dindie, who was pecking nervously at the food on her plate.

After the ladies withdrew, however, Harker grew increasingly expansive, embarking at interminable length upon his experiences as a gay blade of thirty years ago. His consumption of port was phenomenal and the major undertook to replenish his glass at frequent intervals, which had the effect of loosening Harker's tongue to the point of indiscretion.

"Used to be a regular rip," he intoned thickly. "Frequented all the stews. There was one called The Finish . . . " His mouth curved at the recollection. "Kept a pretty line in pullets. Mark my words, get your doxies young — take to new tricks like Lucifer." He focused sourly upon Jamie's brooding countenance. "Tell me, what's a savage about in an English dragoon reg'ment?"

Jamie snatched up their host's empty glass and busied himself at the port, keeping his back towards his sneering tormentor who was now in the altogethery stage of intoxication where every fellow is a friend.

"Jamie's uncle was in the 18th, sir, and bought him a pair of colours. One don't meet many giants in the Light Horse — in fact, we're rather proud to have him in the Droghs." Kit's impudent wink reverted to alarm as Jamie's concoction vanished down Harker's throat. He stared from the bubbling remains in the glass to their host who was slumped insensible on the sofa. "What the blazes did you add to that drink?" he demanded.

"Epsom Salts," replied Jamie laconically. "I just happened to have some with me."

"Jamie, you devil — you planned this beforehand!"

"Maybe." Captain Drummond bent over the recumbent figure and gave a satisfied nod. "Guttered up to his thatch! He'll not stir till morning and then, with any luck, he'll be too occupied to notice Miss Smith is gone."

And indeed by the time that Jervis Harker, clutching his head with one hand and his stomach with the other, felt well enough to heed the enraged bellowing of his sister, the two conspirators with Dindie and Miss Fisher were bowling in a chaise towards Linkdown and Dindie's first ever encounter with Grandfather Hurst.

23

Kit had impressed the necessity of taking no belongings other than what might be carried in a valise. Kate, he said, would provide the balance. Dindie sighed. Since ever she could remember she had been the unwilling recipient of Kate's hand-me-down clothes. Now the resentment and humiliation she had suffered as a child came rushing back.

Under her camlet morning-gown she wore a second garment, her best and only presentable gown with a short red Spencer jacket covering both. Her reticule contained the only valuables she possessed — a gold watch which had belonged to her father and her mama's wedding-ring.

Of the two confrontations which must be endured this meeting with the grandsire who had spurned her from birth aroused the deeper trepidation. Aunt Auden had always shown affection though how she must react to her son's announcement Dindie trembled to think. But Grandfather Hurst was proud and intractable, an old man brooding on the wrongs of the past.

As she stood with Kit in the chilling splendour of the mosaic hall awaiting the butler's summons, a thought so numbing struck Dindie that it almost caused her heart to stop.

"Kit," she stammered, "what if — what if he should disinherit you?" She clung fiercely to his arm. "I shan't marry you if it means estrangement as it did Mama . . . "

"Would you jilt me so readily, my girl?" demanded Kit, with mock severity. The possibility had occurred to him but he could not let her see that the interview was destined to be thorny. He had always been his grandfather's favourite, was, indeed, extremely fond of his irascible relative, yet a decision of this calibre must give undoubted offence, especially as his bride would one day be mistress of Linkdown.

Tucking Dindie's small hand securely through his arm he turned up her face, saying in firm tones, "I promised Grandfather years ago that when I had chosen my wife I should bring her here for his approval. And I'm dashed if I'll go away without his acknowledging you, Dindie. Now let me look you over."

Bravely Dindie mounted the broad staircase on his arm, willing her churning insides to be calm. The butler bowed them into a spacious, book-lined room with long windows extending to floor level. She was permitted only a fleeting glance of admiration at the delicate plasterwork before a gruff voice barked, "Well, boy? Do not hang about! Leg's playing up again, curse it."

This testy stricture emanated from a wing-chair drawn up to one of the windows. A mauve hand extended next, followed by a noble white head wearing a smoking cap. A pair of hawkish eyes swivelled in accusingly.

"God bless me! What have you there?"

Kit greeted this unencouraging utterance with a grin.

"Pleased to find you in such high gig, sir."

Drawing Dindie forward, he stood her before him with one arm reassuringly about her shoulders, and said, "Grandfather, this is Cousin Dorinda. Yesterday I asked her to be my wife and she has done me the very great honour of accepting."

He paused, hoping for some favourable response. He was not fool enough to imagine that this fiercely proud old gentleman would fall upon Dindie with remorse-stricken tears. Sir Roland Hurst was tough as old boots and eighteen years of festering embitterment was a long time.

Quietly he continued, "You will afford us both exceeding happiness, sir, if we may be assured of your blessing."

Dead silence ensued. The hooded eyes screwed into Dindie's. Leaning forward with a plaid wrap about his thin shoulders she fancied him as resembling some crouching bird of prey. Involuntarily, Dindie shrank back.

"Dorinda? Dorinda who?" It was a command.

"D-Dorinda Smith, if you please, sir," she whispered.

There was a sharp intake of breath. The sinewy hands gripped at the arm-rests of the chair. "You . . . are Corinne's girl?"

It was not a question, more a statement of fact. Dindie dropped a trembling curtsy, not daring to look up.

"And you . . . " Sir Roland Hurst fixed a stony eye upon his soldier grandson. "You, sir, have the effrontery to bring this — this person into my house? To parade her as a fitting choice of bride?" His voice erupted in a thunderous roar. "*Get her out of here!* This instant! I will not — "

An ugly growl interrupted his flow. Disgruntled by the shattering of his snooze, a slavering-jawed bulldog got up from the hearth and padded towards Dindie, snuffling horribly. Startled, Dindie dropped her reticule and the animal sank its teeth into the thin material, wheezing wetly at the draw-strings whilst she strove frantically to prise the bag free.

"Caesar! Enough." The bulldog immediately dropped its new toy and sidled back to the hearth. Dindie's relief turned to anguish as the bag's contents spewed through the gaping rent.

"Papa's watch . . . o-oh, no!" The fine chain was snapped beyond repair. Grief-stricken, Dindie sank to her knees on the carpet, cradling the watch in her hands. "It is quite broken . . . " She stared unseeingly before her, fighting to staunch her tears. "He — he was so proud of it. Mama gave it to him, you know "

She looked up at her cousin. "I wanted you to have it, Kit — as a wedding gift. I have n-nothing else to give."

She felt Kit raise her gently, soothing, releasing the watch from her fingers to examine the damage but nothing could ease her desolation.

"Give it here." The gruff intervention startled her. Sir Roland peered at the chain, held the watch to his ear then opened the case to examine the back. "What's it read, hey?"

Dindie wiped at her eyes. "It reads, 'Thine till death'. I think it a beautiful inscription."

"Pah!" The old man snapped shut the watch-case irritably. Now that she could see him at close quarters he did not look so fierce. His lean, aristocratic features must once have been extremely handsome, she decided, and the sharp eyes were grey as Mama's had been. All the Hursts had grey eyes. Dindie alone, with her woeful ordinariness, was pure Smith.

26

Grandfather Hurst tossed the time-piece back to her with a short, triumphant bark. "Pinchbeck! Thought as much. No wonder it snapped so easily. Didn't think my girl would deal out gold hunters to any Tom, Dick or Harry!"

"Grandfather!" White-faced Kit faced his relative. Never could he forgive such a slighting taunt. It was a childish, nasty remark calculated to hurt and totally unworthy, even to one of Sir Rowland's brusque temperament.

He saw Dindie flinch and turn pale. "Go wait for me downstairs. Grandfather and I will discuss this matter as gentlemen."

"Damn your impertinence, boy! I will not be bullied in my own house! Burn this accursed leg!" Sir Roland fell back against the cushions in a paroxysm of rage and pain.

Left alone downstairs Dindie listened to the rise and fall of their heated altercation. She felt drained — the yearning after acceptance, the flicker of reconciliation snuffed out in one insulting taunt.

A person . . . hot tears scalded her eyelids. It was cruel, crushing. Was she not his flesh and blood, as surely his grandchild as Kit or George or Kate? A person . . .

What did it matter if Papa's watch was not real gold? Did he not realise its value was beyond price — that it was the only object left to remind her of that beloved being whom she had adored? And the hurtful part was that their grandfather had realised, and was deliberately setting out to pain and belittle.

A door closed abruptly and her cousin's lithe figure stormed down the broad staircase. His jaw was ominously set and he took her arm almost roughly.

"Kit — what happened?"

"There is no reasoning with him!" Kit strode to the outer door. "I believed he might engage to understand." He stopped, defeat replacing anger on his face. "I'm sorry, Dindie. I did try."

"It does not signify," she whispered, chokily. "Please let us leave now, Kit."

But it did matter, nevertheless. Not merely on her own account

27

but because the incident had brought about a gulf between Kit and his grandfather, and although Dindie tried hard to respond to her cousin's determined efforts at cheerfulness, the suspicion that she must bring him only trouble could not be dispelled.

* * *

They were married three days later in St. James's, Piccadilly. Until such time as it took to acquire a special licence Dindie was settled with Miss Fisher and her sister in the riverside village of Chelsea and the two officers took rooms at Stephen's Hotel. An elaborate ceremony was out of the question. The groomsman was due to report to his regiment by the following Monday and the bridegroom, having missed his sailing at Portsmouth, would have to accompany him and embark with the main convoy. The news must also be broken to Lady Auden, farewells taken and a hundred and one commissions fulfilled before embarkation.

But if the skill of a fashionable modiste was missing, no bride ever looked more radiant than did Dindie that July morning. Her best gown of cream worsted was over-draped by a precious cashmere shawl and her hair was upswept as befitted her new status under quite the smartest bonnet she had ever dared hope to own. It was of cream ribbed silk with a high crown and a curling blue ostrich plume perking over the brim, this last perfectly reconciling her to the banishment of a purple jockey-cap which, her bridegroom sternly assured, would not serve in the least. At her throat she had proudly pinned Kit's especial gift — a brooch worked in gold with the regimental crest of the 18th Hussars set in sapphires and surrounding the whole, the motto *Pro rege, pro lege, pro patria conamur.*

It was an exquisite piece of workmanship and her fingers had trembled with happiness as she fumbled at the clasp. 'For Sovereign, Laws and Country we will strive.' A worthy motto, and one she would be proud to uphold. Smiling, she traced the device of the royal cypher surmounted by the crown and the Roman numerals XVIII. Then she gave a final glance at her pleasing reflection in the glass before picking up her flowers and going downstairs to the waiting carriage.

The ceremony was brief and before Dindie realised, the bells were pealing joyously and she was once more out in the paved forecourt of the church on the arm of her tall husband, receiving a shower of congratulations and good-natured advice from the handful of well-wishers, mainly young officers from Stephen's Hotel, who had determined to give Major Fane a rackety send-off. Miss Fisher cried, her sister begged a flower from the bouquet of hothouse lilies which the groom had almost forgotten to order and Jamie dug his commander in the ribs, muttering that it was customary for a husband to kiss his bride and what did Kit think he was about?

Dindie coloured hotly, pretending inordinate study of the plain gold band on her finger. She sensed Kit's embarrassment, knew that he had perfectly forgotten, perhaps had not even intended to satisfy the expectant gathering in this fashion.

"Why not? Mrs Fane?" Bending his head Kit ducked under the bonnet-brim and kissed her lightly on the mouth, one arm encircling her small waist. For an instant Dindie relaxed against him, eyes closed, then it was over and he was handing her into their coach for the short drive to the Clarendon. Its host Monsieur Jacquiers had prepared a superb bridal déjeuner but when Dindie discovered that the meal was costing Kit four pounds a head with wine an extra guinea, she almost fainted.

*   *   *

"And now you see me hand-fasted, nuptialled and mightily pleased with myself for having surprised you all!"

Kit shot a broad smile across his sister's elegant drawing-room. "Now Mama, I give you leave to indulge in a fit of asterisks if you care. Kate looks as though she is on the fret already," he added, grimacing.

"What else do you expect?" snapped his sister, horror writ large upon her countenance. "Good God, Kit, have you no sense of propriety? We shall be a laughing stock . . . I can never enter Almack's after this! Only consider, Mama — when this affair reaches the *Gazette* we shall have the town by the ears! Kit, how could you?"

"Don't be such a snob, sis," countered Kit, totally unrepentant. "Anyone would think I had wed a painted blackamoor."

"Oh, I declare Dorinda is a well enough match for an attorney or a clergyman, but to have her for a sister!" The Honourable Mrs Farriday flung her brother a glance of utter contempt. "It is unforgivable!"

"I would remind you, Kate, that you are talking of my wife." Kit's eyes held an unexpected steel.

"You had as lief wed the scullery-maid!"

"That will suffice, my dear." The quiet reproof reduced brother and sister to strained silence. Whatever her private feelings, Lady Auden had no intention of adding fuel to the enmity ignited by this bombshell. Extending a hand to her son she said, with a warm smile, "Do not be awakening Dorinda just yet, Kit. She need not feel obliged to join us this evening. The child is exhausted after so eventful a day. Kate, dear . . . "

She inclined her head diplomatically towards the door. Mrs Farriday, who would not have submitted to anyone else, not even her husband, flung Kit a darkling look and flounced from the room, golden curls tossing angrily.

"My dearest boy." Her ladyship embraced her soldier son and drew him down beside her on the flower-embroidered sofa. "I am so proud of you for this chivalrous act."

She gazed mistily at him. "Your cousin is a fine girl . . . but oh, such a child still. I doubt if she is ready to cope with the duties of being a wife."

"I shall encumber her as little as is needful, Mama."

"I do not doubt your sincerity, Kit, but . . . have you seriously considered Dorinda's feelings in this? I was a bride at seventeen myself. It can be a bewildering experience." Lady Auden leaned forward earnestly. "Be gentle with her. She knows nothing of the

30

world as yet. It is for you to guide, Kit. Love and patience will secure the remainder." She regarded him doubtfully. "I suppose you mean to start a family right away?"

"Great Heaven, I've no intention of troubling Dindie in that line, Mama! It would be infamous — besides," he added, firmly, "she is barely out of childhood. You said so yourself."

"I comprehend your reasons, Kit. But will Dorinda?"

The major tightened his lips. "Ours is a marriage of convenience, Mama. Dindie understands that."

"I hope so," returned his Mama, thoughtfully. "Nonetheless, be sensible of her feelings. However dispassionately you may choose to view this union, tonight is your wedding-night and it must be crushing for any bride to learn that her husband does not mean to sleep with her."

Major Fane digested this remark in silence, then he rose abruptly and went upstairs to seek out his young wife.

He found Dindie awake and sitting up in bed, her hair tangled about her shoulders and her face still flushed with the bloom of sleep.

"See, Kit," she laughed, holding up her slipper for his inspection. "I forgot to remove the silver sixpence." She studied the coin, a frown contracting her brows. "Do you really believe it can bring good fortune?"

When he did not answer she glanced up, the brooding intent expression in his eyes filling her with sudden concern. She slipped from bed and ran to him, her bare feet pattering noiselessly across the thick rug.

"Kit, is something amiss? You look so . . . "

He caught her to him, conscious of the vital young body pulsating warmly beneath the simple nightgown. His hands slipped to her waist. She gazed up at him wide-eyed and anxious. Kit smoothed the hair from her brow, keeping an iron rein on the desire stirring within him.

"Nothing is amiss." He took her face between his hands. "Do you think you can be happy with me, wifeling?"

31

She smiled then, her breath escaping in a sigh. "Oh yes. I — I shall try to be a dutiful wife to you, Kit."

His mouth closed upon hers fiercely, startling her with its insistence, then he was carrying her purposefully to the big four-poster bed. His hands moved with practised ease, rendering her powerless. Dindie cried out as she felt the hard strength of his body overwhelm her, drawing her down into a black pit, that same uncharted abyss into which her step-father had brutally forced her. A scream of pure terror rose in her throat, turning her into a struggling, scratching termagant.

Only then did she realise that Kit was frowning down into her face, his eyes dark with concern. His fingers stayed her flailing wrists. She tried to speak but no words would come.

"May Heaven forgive me, Dindie . . . I did not mean to frighten you." Shame-faced, Kit released her. "I shall not come near you again, I swear."

Dindie's face was wet with tears and the painful lump in her throat remained long after he had left her. How could she tell Kit that it was not he whom her body had fought against? How explain that it was not his arms which had closed about her, pinning her inflexibly? It had not been Kit's lips on hers, not his tongue probing, searching her mouth . . .

Would it ever be possible, she wondered bitterly, to blot out the nightmarish memory of that other embrace? The sight of her step-father's bloated, fleshy face, lips slack, the hot stale breath reeking of wine?

Sobbing, Dindie turned her face into the pillow, saturating it with her tears.

3

A HAZY SHEEN of heat obscured the ancient house fronts which towered cliff-like about Lisbon's waterfront. From the Tagus the port expanded like a fan of pearl and ochre and pink, rising in a succession of old tiled roofs, church steeples and palaces to the castle ramparts. Further up-river the square fortress tower of Belem reared white against a cloudless September sky.

Inside British headquarters at Belem three gentlemen stood deep in discussion. The commanding figure by the window was bronzed and extremely good-looking, six feet two of athletic bearing and broad shoulders admirably offsetting the scarlet coat and gold lace of a lieutenant-general. At forty-six, Sir John Moore was at the peak of his career. Born the eldest surviving son of a Glasgow doctor, he had first entered His Majesty's service as a fifteen-year-old ensign and seen hard fighting in North America, Corsica, the West Indies, Ireland, Holland and Egypt. He had escaped death by inches on not a few memorable occasions but never in all his distinguished career had he felt such pent-up frustration and despair as now.

"It's quite settled then?"

Moore nodded slowly. "The terms of the Convention have been agreed to the letter. The French are to evacuate Portugal forthwith."

Colonel Thomas Graham tossed his distinctive mane of silver hair in disgust. "And by ships of the Royal Navy! Was there ever such humiliation? That auld woman Dalrymple has wrecked every advantage of Wellesley's victory at Vimiero with one stroke of a

33

pen!" His eyes flashed contemptuously. "*And* to allow them to carry away their confounded plunder! God sakes, when I think how you would have handled those oily Frog generals — "

"It is desirable that Portugal be cleared of enemy troops immediately and without the necessity of a siege," reminded Moore, gently. "The Convention of Cintra ensures both."

He watched a red-sailed fishing smack wheel slowly and disappear behind a rocky spur of the river. The sticky heat was oppressive. It did not make for even tempers, much less humour the explosive temperament of this, his most senior aide-de-camp. Graham's tenacious loyalty tended to overshadow his judgment but his hatred of the French was consuming. Hardly to be wondered at, mused the general, considering how his beautiful Mary, the celebrated 'Mrs Graham' of Gainsborough's portraits, had been dearer than life to him, a pale, consumptive rose doomed to an early grave.

It had been at Toulouse that Graham, heartbroken with grief, had first conceived that black hatred which was to motivate his life from then on. The lead coffin bearing his wife's remains to interment in Scotland was seized by a mob of drunken Jacobins and its lid wrenched off to expose her waxen, three-week-old corpse, now mutilated and unrecognisable by the ferocity of the attack.

Enough to make any man turn soldier, pondered Moore, but Graham was at that time over forty, a wealthy Perthshire landowner, with no military experience whatsoever. But he had buried his wife, raised a regiment of volunteers, served with distinction and graduated to honorary colonel, driven on by a relentless thirst to crush and destroy the abominated despoilers of his wife's corpse. His friendship with Sir John already spanned fifteen years, a period in which mutual respect and liking had turned into permanent affection. There were few in whom Moore so readily trusted as in this loyal warrior aide.

"I can scarce believe Sir Arthur Wellesley would put his hand to so base an instrument." The quiet interpolation came from the dapper little officer on Moore's left, who until now had remained silent, preoccupied with his own interpretation of the news. "Parliament will be in an uproar. They are bound to call for blood over this capitulation." His dark brooding eyes turned meaningfully on Moore. "That would leave the door open for you, General."

Moore turned from the window, melancholy clouding his face. Paul Anderson's words had unintentionally reopened the wounding memory of that last afternoon in London when the Secretary for War, in the course of conversation, had casually allowed him to learn of his being passed over. The recollection of Castlereagh's coldly impassive features stuck in Moore's mind with perverse stubbornness. At least, he thought with satisfaction, His Lordship little expected the rousing tongue-lashing I left him with. Curse them all he decided grimly. The shame was theirs, not his.

Turning to Colonel Anderson he declared ruefully, "It would be much against my wish to rob General Wellesley of his just reward. Vimiero was brilliantly executed — I only regret we arrived too late to take part. If only Sir Harry Burrard had built on the advantage gained . . . "

If only, he reflected gloomily. His heart went out to Wellesley, over-ruled in his hour of triumph by the leaden hand and brain of bumbling old Sir Harry. Wellesley was the Army's youngest lieutenant-general and unlike himself, popular with the stuffed shirts at the Horse Guards, yet Sir Arthur's dynamic rout of the enemy at Vimiero had so unnerved their aged seniors that Burrard, first on the scene, positively forbade any pursuit of the beaten French. Disgusted and dispirited, Wellesley and his victorious troops had been forced to kick their heels in compliance. Then had come the unexpected French surrender and the botched terms of the Convention, resulting in the astute French representatives running rings so thoroughly around the bemused Sir Hew Dalrymple and his second, that the conditions agreed upon were heavily biased in the enemy's favour, making a mockery of the hard-won peace.

The situation was now gone from bad to worse. Sir Hew seemed incapable of making up his mind what next to do. His original instruction, to dispossess Portugal of the French, had been effected with such speed by Wellesley that he was now at a loss, and to General Moore's suggestion of making contact with the Spanish Junta and certain of their leading generals, as a preliminary to driving the French out of Spain, Sir Hew peevishly replied that the Spanish might not wish for assistance.

Moore suppressed a sigh. Thank God for Graham and the enduring friendship of Paul Anderson. It was quiet-spoken Anderson with his dark Irish looks who had nursed Moore through recurring bouts of fever in the swamps of Santa Lucia during their early campaigning, and it was the devoted vigilance of the little colonel which had saved his friend's life yet again when, badly wounded in Holland, he had mistakenly swallowed a solution of lethal sugar-of-lead.

Beyond the wide sweep of the Tagus, Moore could see the blue heights dotted thickly with tents. His men, like himself, were growing restive with nothing to do. Thankfully, orders had come through for his division to march for Queluz. Even a few miles from the sluggish, stultifying atmosphere of headquarters would be relief.

*   *   *

Dindie leaned back in the creaking carriage as it wound through the Lisbon suburbs past pannier-laden donkeys and balconies bright with carnations and rows of washing. Her eyes ached with the brilliance of the sun on the white walls. She glanced at Kit, seated next her. What were his thoughts? she wondered apprehensively.

His mouth was set in a firm line. She could almost feel his tense anxiety as the dusty road ate up the miles to Queluz. She tried not to think of his coolness, of the total inadequacy of their relationship. So much had happened since leaving England.

At first it had been a whirl of excitement. The high-masted transports riding at anchor fascinated her, and when finally she stepped on deck with Kit she had given herself wholeheartedly to this beckoning new world of sheet and spar and sun-bright water. Kit took her off to watch the troop-horses being put in the slings, and it was then she had noticed them — army wives, gaunt with weariness, clinging wordless to their menfolk on the quayside. These women, Dindie knew, had trudged with their husbands every mile of the way from Rochester, but why did they look so despairing and drawn, and for what purpose was the troop-sergeant admitting them by turns to a hut near the embarkation point, only to have them emerge sobbing hysterically into the waiting arms of their menfolk? It was harrowing, disturbing. She must know the reason.

"They are conducting the ballot," explained Kit quietly. "It's a wretched business, Dindie. You don't want to watch."

He placed a hand under her elbow but she remained stubbornly rigid, her youthful face pale and troubled.

"What happens?" she whispered.

"Every time a regiment is ordered overseas, lots are drawn in the ranks to settle which wives are to travel with their men. The Army, you see, permits only a maximum of six from each troop or company and they should have no children to be eligible."

"Is that what is being done now? Drawing lots?"

Kit nodded. " 'To go' is scribbled six times on slips of paper and the remaining slips are marked 'Not to go'. They are put into the nearest cap and given a good stir, and the door is then opened to allow the poor wretches from each company in turn to learn their fate." His mouth tightened. "Basic and brutal. But this way there can be no question of bias."

He saw her eyes darken in horror and immediately slipped an arm about her shoulder, saying gently, "It *is* harsh, I own. But one must be objective, Dindie."

She fought off his restraining hand. "How can you speak of it so — so complacently? Why, I never saw anything so barbarous . . . "

Tears filled her eyes, blurring the scene but nothing could shut out the hopeless sobbing of the 'Not to go's'. One woman in particular, a girl not much older than herself, had fainted and was being tended by her husband, a young private whom Dindie recognised as being in Captain Jones's troop.

"Who are they?" she whispered.

"His name is Hunt. They married in secret only a few weeks ago, I believe."

Dindie stared at the wretched girl slumped against her youthful husband. Now that she was on her feet the couple's haste to be wed was all too apparent. The girl was far gone with child and her time could not be long off. She had a glazed, stunned look about her, unable even to weep. There was no need to ask which way the ballot had gone.

In that moment, Dindie thanked God that Kit held a commission. But for the crimson of an officer's sash she too must have joined that pitiable queue at the ballot with a palpitating heart and fear tearing her insides.

"Is there no other means of selection?" she asked, scrubbing guiltily at her eyes, aware that Kit abhorred tears of all things.

"None," he returned, shortly. "That is why Colonel Stewart orders the ballot to be left until the last possible moment. Even if it were permissible to select by rote the numbers would still have to remain at six. Either way . . . "

Either way the end result would be the same. He did not add that the majority of the luckless faced starvation or prostitution — there was no middle road. And most would never see their husbands again. It was no coincidence that the regimental band was drawn up in waiting. The rousing strains of 'Garryowen' or 'The young May moon' would effectively drown the agonised screams of the demented creatures left on shore.

Dindie was roused from reflection by Kit's hand on her arm.

"We have arrived," he murmured, pointing ahead.

Dindie looked, and exclaimed in delight. She knew from Kit that Queluz had been a former royal palace, but never had she visualised anything so perfect. A miniature Versailles with walls pink as a wild rose, Queluz was charmingly set in grounds laid out

38

in the formal French manner with walks of clipped boxwood and fountains tinkling.

"It's a palace of pink sugar," she breathed.

Kit fastened the top button of his tunic with meticulous care. "It's Sir John Moore's headquarters," he retorted bluntly. "And I am four weeks late."

The screech of carriage wheels and the clatter of sword on stone steps caused Captain George Napier to glance up from securing his horse's girth. Curiosity changed to a wide grin of recognition.

"Fane! Good to see you at last! They've turned you into a major, I believe." He straightened, black eyes dancing wickedly. "Lord, I ought really to be sir-ing you. It's going to be devilish work remembering — " He stared beyond Kit to Dindie, who stood nervously fingering her bonnet-strings, and raised an eyebrow enquiringly to the major.

"I got married," explained Kit quietly, introducing his young wife.

Dindie coloured under the candid approval of this self-assured six-footer who, she learned, was another of the general's aides and an officer in Moore's own regiment, the 52nd. She already knew from Kit that this was one of the three crack rifle regiments trained by General Moore at Shorncliffe Camp in Kent and as the famous Light Brigade were the Army's elite in discipline and modern technique.

Napier's friendly overtures broke any lingering reserve. He looked, thought Dindie, like some burning-eyed young eagle, with his arresting classical nose and olive-skinned blackness, but she liked him on sight. He was staring at her with a peculiar expression.

"I beg your pardon. You remind me awfully of someone I know." Napier flashed her an apologetic smile and turned to Kit. "I had better conduct you to the chief right away. He's nippy as Hades — so be warned."

*　　*　　*

"Married?" Moore's eyebrows snapped upwards. Behind the elegant desk of Honduras mahogany his features remained immovable. "Major Fane, I had hopes that every gentleman holding a commission would appreciate the irresponsibility of embarking on such a venture at this time!" His jaw hardened.

"When I chose you to join my personal staff I did so because of your outstanding record as a regimental officer, because I was confident of your ability to execute the duties with honour and, above all, because of your sound common sense. In this latter virtue it would seem I was mistaken."

Folding his arms, the general surveyed the young major standing smartly to attention before him. "I should be obliged for an explanation," he invited, with heavy courtesy. "She must be a remarkable lady to have engaged your affections so particularly."

"She's my cousin, sir." Kit felt the all-seeing hazel eyes burn his very soul. Their directness demanded total honesty in return. It was not mere anger he read there. Moore's disappointment outweighed all else, piercing Kit's leaden spirits like a lash.

The long room behind him was breathtaking in magnificence, but its painted ceilings and frescoed flower garlands were a blur. He could think only of Dindie waiting anxiously for him on the other side of the gilded doors, see again her unspoken plea to keep faith. Looking his new commander squarely in the eye, Kit said, "She is very young, sir, and — it was vital we get married before I sailed."

"You haven't got her into trouble, I hope?" The unbargained-for question shook Kit with its directness.

"No, sir!"

Sir John's face broke into a grin almost boyish in its candour.

"Thank Heaven for that! What took you so long to get here? Your furlough was at an end last month. I should like to know how you saw fit to extend it."

Beneath the lightened tone Kit recognised heavy censure. The general was renowned for his fairness but he was nobody's fool. Briefly Kit recounted everything, in the certain knowledge that Dindie's unhappy history would go no further.

Moore remained silent for some minutes, then he stood up and extended an outstretched hand. "Thank you for being so frank with me, Fane. When a man once lies to me I've done with him! Now," discarding all reserve, "when do I have the honour of being presented to your lady?"

"She's waiting outside, sir."

In spite of her trepidation, Dindie was curious to meet this great soldier whom Kit and Jamie, and indeed every other officer, regarded with a devotion verging on hero worship. Her initial impression was of a very tall, manly figure whose curling brown hair was greying ever so slightly in front. As he stepped forward to greet her, the quizzing interest in his glance altered — she would never know how to describe the reaction — and he stood rooted, the colour draining from his face, staring at her as if at a ghost.

Dindie turned in bewilderment from George Napier, who had shown her in, to her husband but Kit was equally mystified and disconcerted. Then, as though recollecting himself, the general bowed over her hand and murmured a welcome, but his pallor was strongly accentuated and he was clearly striving to master his feelings.

Dindie observed the keen glance he exchanged with Captain Napier. Courteously he expressed the hope that they would meet again at dinner, before striding swiftly back to his desk with an expression rock-hard and unfathomable.

It was George Napier who broke the silence that followed. Closing the double doors behind them he turned to Dindie, saying with quiet apology, "You reminded him of my cousin Caroline."

*   *   *

In the palatial writing-room smelling of beeswax, Sir John Moore stared through one of the long windows that overlooked the leafy alleys with their stone sphinxes. All the old longings were come surging back to torture him, when he had thought them

41

dead. That girl! So fresh-faced, so full of shy charm . . . He leaned his brow against the cool glass closing his eyes tight. So like his beloved Caroline in looks and colouring that for a moment he had thought . . . They were of an age, yet when he considered their similarity he knew it for an illusion. The child-bride just introduced to him had an appealing, turn-up nose whereas Caroline's was straight, her hair darker, her eyes . . .

He had first made the acquaintance of Miss Caroline Fox on a hot Sicilian day two years previously, although he had known her general father some considerable time and was indeed in that summer of 1806 appointed to be his second-in-command. The most affectionate of Papas, General Fox had from their nursery days delighted to show off the miniatures of his two lovely little daughters. It came as a thunderbolt to Moore to reconcile this sparkling brunette, who reached not even to his shoulder, with the child of his fancy.

They were thrown considerably in each other's society that summer. More so, after the following April when her elder sister Louisa married, leaving Miss Caroline to entertain General Moore, for whom the Fox domestic circle at Messina was quickly becoming a second home. This sixteen-year-old charmer, with her quick mind and bubbling exuberance, above all with her adorable innocence, succeeded in doing what no woman had managed before. For the first time Moore found himself hopelessly in love, done for by the entrancing smile and expressive brown eyes of a girl not yet seventeen.

It was madness, impossible! For all the mature airs she was a child still, and he thirty years her senior! His agony had been acute, his spirit in dark conflict between duty and the fire of longing. In all his life he had never known such passion as he now felt towards this charming miss who brought all the freshness and promise of youth to a war-wearied veteran. He wanted a hearth of his own . . . a bright-eyed someone to come home to. He knew her parents approved, knew she herself would accept him without demur. But he had hesitated to declare himself. When the butterfly

42

was fairly emerged from the chrysalis, if a younger fellow should happen by, what then? Must she not bitterly repent her youthful judgment, imprisoned in marriage to a husband old enough to be her father?

Moore had wrestled with these torturing doubts a thousand times through the hot Sicilian nights at Palermo and Messina, where the scent of orange blossom hung heavy in the air; where fireflies danced shimmering-bright and the plash of an oar on moonlit water or the delicate fluttering of a hawk-moth alone intruded. In the future whenever he thought of Sicily he was to remember the fireflies . . . vibrant, beautiful as the sweet Caroline whom he must will himself to forget.

With an effort he returned to his desk and took up his pen. It would not have served, he told himself sternly, and dipped his quill so fiercely in the ink-pot that an angry blot spurted over the half-written page.

*   *   *

Within the next two weeks Dindie found herself caught up in a confusing round of new faces, places and experiences. With the exception of elderly Colonel Graham, the 'family' of aides-de-camp at the general's headquarters were, like George Napier, dashing, high-spirited young officers in their twenties who delighted to vie with each other in making her feel welcome. In their free time they took her sightseeing in Lisbon, a city which Dindie, after her first startled sight of the public delousing which went on in its streets, became convinced must be unrivalled both in beauty and sheer filth. Napier and Harry Percy undertook to teach her the latest dance steps and struggled with rueful good humour to keep pace with her determination to master the Portuguese language, the intonation of which, with its fascinating rise and fall, was both complex but rewarding when her halting attempts were understood by the local townspeople.

But Jamie would always be her favourite and his quiet pleasure in her society when she accompanied Kit to Belem made up a good deal for the hurt and loneliness she tried so hard to conceal. Her imagination was fired when he showed her round the beautiful Moorish monastery and cloisters situated near the regiment's quarters there. But not even to Jamie could she unburden herself.

Since their wedding-night when she had rebuffed him so hurtfully, so — so unpardonably, Kit had made it plain that he would not again lay himself open to rejection. Never by so much as a word did he refer to the bleak incident but his manner towards her betokened polite indifference. She was his to protect, she might wear his ring but in no real terms was she his wife and although to outsiders their relationship might appear equable, Dindie knew that beneath the easy-going pretence Kit was still very angry.

The flame of his wrath had been rekindled during their voyage out. That first day at sea Kit had made her promise not to venture below decks where the troops and their wives were quartered. But after the first wretched days of sea-sickness she had felt well enough to leave the dark, fetid state-room which she shared with another officer's lady and look about her. It was meal-time and the wooden hatchways were unbattened, and her natural curiosity to discover what lay beyond had been intensified by an infant's shrill wail.

She was unprepared for the overwhelming stench of urine and rank sweat. What little air permeated the gloomy lower deck was befouled and hot with the breath and bodily functions of cot upon cot of blue-coated dragoons. Trestle tables were slung from the beams at intervals and in one corner the men and their wives were queuing up with mess tins under the supervision of an N.C.O. to receive the regulation dollop of salt beef and ship's biscuit.

"You're Major Fane's lady, ain't you?" The voice was Cockney, faintly hostile. "What you come down 'ere for, then? We ain't no bleedin' side-show, ducks."

The woman's question was echoed silently in a score of neighbouring eyes, some curious, most lethargic, uncaring.

Dindie's heart pounded apprehensively. She was well aware she ought not to have come. Flushing crimson she replied, in halting tones.

"I heard a baby crying." She glanced about her, biting her lip. "I — I do not mean to intrude. Whose baby do you suppose . . . "

The woman pushed back a strand of dark hair from her face and laughed unexpectedly. "Well, it weren't mine, that's certain."

She laid one hand flat across her stomach and Dindie saw for the first time that her questioner was well advanced in pregnancy.

"I'm a three-month an' more near me time, Gawd 'elp me, and where we'll find ourselves by then I hates to think!"

"Sure, the darlin' mite will come easy as drawin' rabbits from a silk hat, Mrs Baillie. Have I not bore five myself an' two more that the good Lord seed fit to take to his own?"

"Will you hark at Sadie O'Flynn? She'll not be tellin' the major's lady of them four darlin' mites she seed fit to stop with the 'elp of Madame Geneva!"

Dindie listened in perplexity to this exchange. The women were pressing close but they were not unfriendly. For the most part they were youngish, although their hard upbringing was evident in prematurely shadowed eyes and general undernourishment. The Irishwoman, Mrs O'Flynn, had the dragged-down, haggard look so familiar in those of Papa's patients who had produced too many children in rapid succession. Indeed, the infant sucking at her breast could not be more than three months old.

Dindie touched the baby's soft cheek with the back of her fore-finger. The hungry mouth stopped in surprise and the baby gazed at her with solemn, unblinking eyes. Then he stuck a tiny fist in his mouth and buried his head on his mother's neck.

Dindie longed to hold him. She loved babies, delighted in their squirming perfectness. Instead, she let curiosity conquer reserve and asked, "Please — who is this Madame Geneva? Is she a midwife?"

The women stared at her then a raucous shout of laughter reverberated on all sides. Mrs O' Flynn dumped the protesting mite at her breast into the arms of an older child and sat herself heavily on a wooden crate to enjoy the joke.

"Madame Geneva? Lord 'elp me, that's rich."

The woman whom the others called Mrs Baillie wiped at her streaming eyes. "Why, she's the best midwife of all, ducks! Madame Geneva is what we calls a drop o' Jackey — gin to the likes of you, Mrs Fane." She regarded Dindie with an incredulous stare. "Ain't you ever 'eard of hot gin for makin' away with unwanteds?"

Dindie shook her head, wide-eyed. All the lying-ins attended by Papa had been orthodox where the babies were long hoped for or at worst accepted with resignation. It had never occurred to her that some women might not wish to conceive a child, might indeed, resort to the desperate and wholly wicked practice discussed so matter of factly by these soldiers' wives . . . *Hot gin!* Dindie would have liked to learn more but the horrific nature of it all, this destroying of life not yet born so over-powered her that she was reduced to silence.

Turning to the Irishwoman, at whose skirts a couple of toddlers were whimpering, she asked eagerly, "Please may I cuddle your baby for a little, Mrs O'Flynn?"

*   *   *

Kit sat alone in the spacious ante-room used by the aides as an office. Through the open window the drone of bees on fragrant oleander drifted up to him as he worked. It was almost noon and in the claustrophobic heat his uniform weighed heavily. Napier was gone into Lisbon to purchase a sabre, the colonel had ridden over to General Fraser's division and Harry Percy, whose capacity for falling in love was a standing joke at headquarters, had sauntered off to the kitchens in search of a pretty, black-eyed *rapariga* who had engaged his attentions.

The work-load had increased enormously these last two days now that Sir Hew Dalrymple had been summoned home. It was rumoured there was to be a court of inquiry held in Chelsea Hall over the mortifying Cintra Convention. It was a pity, thought Kit, that Wellesley too must be implicated, for many believed his hand had been forced over the business.

Major Fane's paperwork was interrupted by the entrance of a breathless courier bearing a despatch from England, to be delivered immediately to General Moore.

"I'll see to it." Kit rose smartly.

Sir John Moore broke the seal and scanned the despatch quickly then without a word passed it to the major. It was from Lord Castlereagh, the Secretary for War, worded in the usual crisp ministerial style and had been eleven days in transit. Its content caused Kit to catch his breath.

> Downing Street
> September 25th, 1808
>
> Sir,
>
> His Majesty having determined to employ a corps of his troops, of not less than 30,000 infantry and 5,000 cavalry in the North of Spain to co-operate with the Spanish armies in the expulsion of the French from that kingdom, has been graciously pleased to entrust to you the Command in Chief of this Force.

"But this is splendid news, sir! Now we shall have a real chance of drubbing the French!"

Moore was smiling broadly. "There has been no such command since Marlborough for a British officer! Fane, you and I are going to celebrate." Striding to a decanter he measured two glasses of wine, his face elated. "I hope to Heaven I may justify your confidence. I confess myself dumbfounded."

Setting down his glass he read over the communication once again, an expression hard to interpret sobering his countenance.

"I was convinced they would give something brilliant to Sir Arthur," he murmured, almost to himself. Then the boyish smile reasserted itself. "How they came to pitch upon *me* I cannot say, for you know as well as I they have given sufficient proof of not being partial to me."

His keen eye swept the long room, dwelling on the lavish decoration recently completed by the French General Junot. Imperial eagles straddled the ceilings crushing underfoot the crowns and broken sceptres of Europe. Every niche was a tribute to the Emperor with the letter 'N' enclosed in victory wreaths. Only the gold plate was missing. Junot's troops had methodically sacked Queluz prior to their hasty exit.

Moore's reflections, however, were far from his imposing surroundings. From being the outcast general of the British Army he was now its commander-in-chief. What price now Castlereagh's wounding snubs? Hoist with their own petard, he thought, permitting himself a grim smile. They had hoped to force his hand, leave him no alternative but to resign . . . they had not conceived it possible that he might call their bluff and accept the demeaning employment offered of serving in a subordinate capacity with the very troops he had lately commanded as chief. How there must be a gnashing of teeth in Downing Street! They had appointed him only because they had presumably run out of excuses. He was next in line of seniority — and there was no one else to put forward.

If he had not known Wellesley to be still at sea when the despatch was dated, Moore would have attributed the hook-nosed little general's influence no small factor in this radical change of fortune, for at their unexpected meeting two weeks ago, that aloof character had bluntly stated his intention of underlining to Lord Castlereagh the disastrous brink to which Dalrymple and Burrard had brought the Army. Moore, he affirmed, must be their natural successor.

"To your well-deserved appointment, sir. My stars, this is a settler and no mistake!" Kit's eyes burned with relish. He could scarce wait to tell Dindie.

Sir John acknowledged the enthusiastic response but did not drink immediately. His expression altered and he said quietly, "You do realise, Fane, that they have entrusted to me not merely a considerable part of our fighting force. It is in fact *the* British Army. I pray I may be able to acquit myself as becomes me — for if I fail our country will be left utterly undefended."

4

IT WAS NATURAL that the new commander-in-chief should be obliged to entertain and be entertained on a grander scale than formerly. For reasons of accommodation, Major Fane and his lady were temporarily settled in a lodge in the palace grounds under the tender mercies of a garlic-breathing virago.

From the outset it was plain that Senhora Ribera resented the intrusion. Her manner was disenchantment bordering on insolence. The room to which she assigned them was not only meagre — it had been denuded of furniture save for the compulsory appointments of something to lie on, a wash-stand, water and a towel. Only a wooden crucifix had been suffered to remain on the walls as safeguard against the heathen English.

Whilst Kit was at headquarters Dindie unpacked their few belongings. Items not immediately required would be stowed with the Baggage far to the rear once the march inland commenced and thereafter not made available until they reached Spain.

With infinite care she hung her husband's dress jacket over the only chair in the room, grooming the dark blue face-cloth industriously with a stiff brush. It was quite the smartest of all the cavalry uniforms, decided Dindie loyally, allowing her fingers to run lightly over the intricate lace and facings. Much more smart, to her mind, than the scarlet staff coat which he wore most days.

He had last worn full dress on their wedding-day. She rested one cheek against the garment, desolation washing over her afresh. It was all so vivid still . . . the hushed church with its splendid carving over the altar, the blue ribbon and sprig of myrtle woven through her flowers for luck, her moment of pure joy when the blessing was pronounced and she had gazed shyly into Kit's eyes, thinking proudly how well his uniform became him and how happy they were about to be.

But her dreams had been short-lived, ground to dust in the harsh reality of their domestic situation. 'A season of sad willow' . . . the words of a half-remembered poem mocked her despairing thoughts. Was this how their marriage was to be? Punctuated with tears and recrimination?

Biting her lip she crossed to the wash-basin and laid out his razor and shaving strop. She held a tablet of Windsor soap to her nose, inhaling the delicate scent of lavender. She had bought it from Smyth's the Bond Street perfumers, and it had been her first purchase for him as a wife.

She considered whether or not to seek out their landlady to request extra bedclothes. Senhora Ribera had provided sheets and a worked flounced quilt but no blankets and with the onset of October the temperatures cooled remarkably at nights. Dindie decided to wait. Kit might construe her action as an abuse of hospitality and she dreaded to inflame their quarrel still more.

It had begun so innocently. After their stormy sea passage the troop-horses had rapidly lost condition. Kit was especially worried about his own black stallion Bob, so much weakened that the animal could barely stand. Dindie had been at the rails with Jamie waiting for the pinnace to take them ashore for their first sight of Lisbon when Kit joined them, delivering her an irritable rebuke for an intemperate peal of laughter at some remark of Jamie's.

How could she have suspected then how secretly worried he was at the grave danger of fever breaking out aboard the crowded transport through the insanitary horrors endured by the men? Piqued and embarrassed she turned to Jamie and bestowed him a warm smile to the deliberate exclusion of her husband.

"How I wish you will not address me as Mrs Fane, Jamie. It

sounds altogether matronly and stiff-necked. I had rather you call me Dindie, as Kit does."

Major Fane's brows immediately snapped together and his eyes distinctly intimated that he had a very different name in mind for his wife at that moment, but he remained tight-lipped whilst she prattled on without once glancing his way.

"Jamie," she said, thoughtfully. "How soon will the enlisted men be allowed on shore? Some wives have babies on board, you know. Oh, I perfectly realise they must have been smuggled past the duty officer — but what of that?"

She caught Kit's eye upon her and a little devil within prompted her to add, scornfully, "My husband entertains the most profound regard for King's Regulations. You may be sure that if *he* were embarkation officer there would be no contravening of the Articles!"

"You are being provokingly unfair, Dindie!" Kit's manner was dangerously polite. "Officers are human, believe it or not. I have turned a blind eye to stowaway wives and their brats before now!"

"That is how you may dismiss them, I dare say!" she retorted, hotly. "Just so many troublesome extra mouths to be fed." She saw his eyes flash but she was too angry to heed. "There are wives below deck with babies at the breast! There are children hardly breeched who are obliged to breathe the noxious stench of ammonia from your abominable stables!"

"I am uncomfortably aware of the fact but how do you come to know it?"

Kit spoke the words quietly, so quietly that she was unprepared. She felt the keenness of his glance and a hot flush burned her cheeks. The incriminating silence lengthened until Dindie could bear it no longer. In a small voice she heard herself say, "I — I have been there, Kit. That is how I know."

His indrawn exclamation reverberated in her ears like a knell. Trembling, Dindie nerved herself to meet his face.

"You have been in contact with the men?"

51

Dismay and anger at her deceit exploded within Kit. With one stride he caught her close, gripping her shoulders ungently.

"*You little fool!* Did I not expressly forbid such a thing? How many times were you there, Dindie? In Heaven's name, answer me! *How often?*"

"Twice," she whispered, close to tears. "Kit — you are hurting me."

His grip relaxed. She felt his eyes burn her face, then relief induced in him a flood of anger which he seemed powerless to check.

"When I request you to refrain from certain action, Madam, I expect to be obeyed! It is no concern of yours to be traipsing out of bounds!" His mouth compressed grimly. "Why did you, Dindie?"

Choking she stammered, "I wanted to play with the babies . . . see for myself how they did. I — I did not imagine any harm could be done. And I repent none of it!" she concluded, with a flash of defiance. "How can Colonel Stewart condone such — such infamous conditions?"

Unheeding the empty coldness in his face she rushed on, heatedly, "*He* is not obliged to queue every morning at the urine-bucket! If any one officer amongst you was forced to endure a single night in that verminous cage — "

Immediately she realised she had gone foo far. Her abominable tongue! Jamie was looking uncomfortable and the sailors holy-stoning and swabbing the decks with vinegar had paused to listen and exchange sly winks. Most of all was she conscious of Kit's quiet fury. He regarded her steadily for a long moment then with awful civility gave her his arm along the wet deck for the short trip to shore.

Sighing, Dindie pushed the incident from her mind. She washed her hair and took a bath, revelling in the pleasure of feeling scrupulously clean. It was not, of course, what in England consti-tuted a proper ablution; Dindie doubted if Senhora Ribera had even heard of a sitz-bath. When they had moved in their belongings that morning Kit had fashioned a make-shift screen across the room so as to block off the wash area. It was only a length of canvas folded over a rope but Dindie was grateful for his consideration. Had he guessed her disquiet at the prospect of undressing and bathing in front of him? She blushed to herself. If Kit privately ridiculed her inhibitions he gave no sign.

She glanced over the rough screen to the bed in the corner. How would it feel, she wondered, to lie in his arms? She turned quickly away, knowing with a pricking of tears that she was unlikely to discover the answer. A marriage of convenience — that was the basis of their relationship and she would cause herself less heartache if she remembered it. With fierce determination Dindie towelled her damp hair and reached for the flimsy wrapper which Kate had bequeathed her along with several other items from her wardrobe.

A creaking noise suddenly alerted Dindie to the fact that she was not alone. Standing on tiptoe she peeped over the lightly slung canvas and saw with alarm that her landlady had entered the room closely followed by two of her daughters. They were clearly under the impression that both she and Kit were gone out, for there was much exclaiming and examining of their possessions.

Even as Dindie stared, unsure what to make of this intrusion, Senhora Ribera discovered Kit's dolman jacket hanging over the chair. In rapid Portuguese she called excitedly to her girls and they surrounded the garment, gesticulating and fingering the rich embellishments with loud exclamations. The elder girl Carlotta bit hard on the shiny buttons with her teeth but when she then whipped scissors from the châtelaine at her waist and began to hack at the buttons in frenzied fashion, Dindie uttered a cry of horror and dashed from concealment, struggling to fasten the wrapper about her as she did so.

"Stop! *Stop* it, I tell you! What are you about?"

Pushing aside the astonished girl she snatched up the garment and held it against her breast, defying the trio to come near. "How dare you walk in and — and behave so!" she quivered, hearing her voice tremble with anger on the words. "Go away — all of you!"

Senhora Ribera advanced a couple of steps, her shrewd black eyes darting from the shining buttons to Dindie's resolute face. She was a big woman and the funereal black so beloved of her countrywomen made her resemble some awesome, hovering tarantula. Hands flailing the air she erupted in a frightening torrent of Portuguese, of which Dindie understood not a word but from the manner of delivery and the derisive laughter of the two younger women she was in no doubt of the hostility behind it.

"Oh, please . . . " she pleaded, feverishly trying to recall the elementary phrases she had taught herself earlier.

"*Por favor . . . Não compreendo!* Oh, I beg you will leave me be!"

"Dindie."

Kit stood in the doorway surveying the drama, one hand outstretched towards her. How long he had been present Dindie did not know. Uttering a little cry she ran to him burying her face in his breast, relief overwhelming her.

"Hush, now." His voice was surprisingly gentle.

"Kit — they tried to take your buttons!"

She raised her head and saw that he was smiling.

"No, is that so?" Releasing her hand he bade her stand aside and with unexpected swiftness half drew his sabre from its belt demanding, in a loud voice, "*Desejo que a senhora vá!*"

Senhora Ribera immediately spat derisively in his face, emitting a screech of vituperation which might have been heard in Lisbon.

"You impertinent crone!" Half amazed, half laughing, Kit strode towards her menacingly. The sight of that curved blade unsheathed and glinting proved too unnerving even for the bull-eyed landlady. With a blood-curdling shriek she bundled her daughters before her with indecent haste, and their combined screams for aid to the Holy Mother echoed long after their exit.

"Well, I'm damned if ever the Regulations list a penalty for

54

thieving billet-tenders! Does she imagine we are lodged here for our own enjoyment? They will dance to a different tune if Bonaparte re-takes Lisbon!"

Kit unbuckled his sword with an expression of disgust and peeled off his jacket. He glanced across at his young wife standing motionless by the window.

"Come here, Dindie," he called softly.

She came and stood hesitantly before him, her hair curling damply about her forehead. He saw it and frowned.

"Bless me, you're practically naked! Go fetch some garments this instant."

"I'm not cold. Kit . . . " Pleadingly she faced him, overpower-ingly conscious of his closeness." Say you have forgiven me! I — I realise our quarrel was my fault and I have longed so much to apologise."

"Oh, *Dindie*." He spoke the words softly and held out his hands, palms upwards. She laid her own small hands in his, her body atingle with the sharpness of longing.

"I had no notion my wife had such spirit," murmured Kit, laying his cheek against her sweet-smelling hair. "I honestly believe you would have torn out their eyes on account of my poor dolman."

She lifted her face. "They would have cut off your buttons!"

"I daresay they mistook them to be silver-plated." He placed a finger under her chin. "I'm proud of you, Dindie."

"*Are you*, Kit? Then — then you are not sorry that you married me?"

He stared. "*Sorry?* Good grief, of course I'm not sorry! But I did wrong to bring you here, Dindie. Campaign life is harsh for a woman and will become progressively worse if the weather breaks."

"I shall prove equal to whatever discomforts the march may bring," she declared fiercely.

Her resolution brought a smile to Kit's lips.

"You are laughing at me!" accused Dindie, hotly.

"No, upon my honour!" He held her at arm's length, his expression altering. "You're good for me, Dindie. You are impulsive and kittenish and — and fiercely loyal and anxious to please . . . " His voice failed unexpectedly. Looking up, Dindie was horrified to see a suspicion of tears in his eyes.

"*Kit!*" Now that her sight was sharpened she recognised a tautness about his mouth, and his face was greyish beneath its tan. "Kit — are you unwell?" Fear clutched her insides.

"It's Bob." He sat heavily on the bed, his voice expressionless. "I had to do it, Dindie. His legs . . . scabrous all over."

"Oh, Kit . . . I *am* sorry."

She slipped to her knees before him aching to comfort, yet not knowing how. She knew him to be an expert shot and the animal must have felt no pain, but to say so would not make him feel any less its executioner. "Where will you find another mount?"

"There is to be a local fair tomorrow at Paço d'Arcos, not far from here. I fancy there will be bloodstock on offer. We must fix you up with a horse, come to that."

"Will there be booths and tumblers, Kit? Oh, do say you will take me along!" Her eyes met his in wistful pleading.

"Well, of course I mean to take you, wifeling."

Kit pulled off his boots and stretched out yawning on the bed. "Lord, I'm done for. Been in the saddle all day." He turned over, watching her as she combed her hair to one side so that it fell in a soft curtain about her shoulders. "It's not the same on a borrowed mount," he added, tightly, closing his eyes.

Dindie knelt before the charcoal *brasero*. "Did I tell you I encountered General Moore today, Kit? I was by the fountain with the stone dolphins and we had such a lovely talk! He keeps a journal — did you know? I mean to do the same, so I may have a record of all the places we pass through on the march — "

She saw that he had fallen asleep, one arm flung out awkwardly on the hard pillow. There were dark circles under his eyes and his hair was tousled. Gently Dindie drew the quilt up to his chin and stood for some minutes in contemplation of the strong mouth, the barely perceptible stubble at his chin.

Slipping off the wrapper she donned her simple white shift and crossed to the window. A single star hung over the distant heights. It was there, over those beckoning violet mountains that their route of march lay.

The last embers of coal glowed fiercely in the iron embrasure. Dindie slipped into bed and snuggled close to Kit's back, listening in the half-dark to his deep, rhythmic breathing. Please God, she prayed silently, make everything come right between us. Then she too slept.

* * *

They talk of my going into Spain as though it were Hyde Park! This frustrated observation, confided in correspondence earlier that day, stuck in Moore's mind for many hours after, for it so aptly summed up the naivety of the Government's thinking. He had been left an unenviable legacy. The Peninsular venture was proving to have been grossly ill-conceived from the outset. The Treasury had even fallen down upon its assurance to supply him with gold bullion, leaving him a mere twenty-five thousand pounds in his military chest to pay both his troops and the cost of hiring transport and pack-mules.

Moore's anxiety over transport was increased by the knowledge that he must get across the mountains before the torrential rains of autumn turned the rutted tracks to quagmires. For the march into Spain he must also split up his army into separate routes, not merely for safety's sake but because the strain of supporting such a concentrated force upon the local countryside would be considerable. He was hampered, moreover, by a Commissariat ill-trained and virtually ineffective, and by another major problem of feeding in quite another direction.

"Women and children! Droves of them!" exclaimed Kit in exasperation to George Napier, unsaddling his steaming horse after a trying morning spent at Belem. "It's not to be supposed a redcoat should be celibate but hang me! Estimates must be met and accounts balanced."

"That's rich, coming from you," commented Napier, with a sly grin." If I had a love of a wife like Dindie burning for my return at nights you'd not hear me complain!"

"I dare say. But Dindie is only here because there was no possibility of leaving her in England, and I don't have any brats that I know of," retorted Kit, wondering what Napier would say if he knew the true situation with Dindie.

"Well, there ought to be an improvement soon. The chief has just drafted an Order giving wives the chance to be shipped home before the hardships of the campaign overtake 'em."

But few women accepted the offer to remain behind, the majority arguing they had rather stick by their men and march over the mountains with their children than endure the threat of going on the Parish back in England. Many had been disowned by outraged parents, for the stigma attached to marrying one of the debased soldiery was strong. Remain they would, come hail, hell or Bonaparte.

The day following publication of this Order saw the first regiments leave Queluz camp to follow the line of march along the banks of the Tagus. The cavalry and heavy guns would take the route through Badajoz, link up with the main force at a point in the plains of Castile and move on together for Valladolid where the reinforcements now being despatched from England under General Baird would be waiting for them.

After dictating a series of directives to his military secretary John Colborne, the commander-in-chief took up his pen to write to Lady Hester Stanhope. This niece of Mr Pitt, the former Prime Minister, had been a staunch champion and confidante for many years and if at times she was inclined, like all intellectuals, to be domineering, her rank independence, her wit and warm distaste of pomposity found a kindred spirit in Jack Moore.

She was now two-and-thirty but in an age when women were considered on the shelf at twenty-one Hester would merely shrug, maintaining stoutly that she had rather have been born a man anyhow, and a soldier most of all.

It was her abiding joy that the profession of arms had been embraced by her favourite half-brother Charles. He was a major with the 50th Regiment and had already served as aide to Moore in Sicily. She would be immensely satisfied to learn that Charles was, after all, to accompany the march to Spain. The 50th Regiment was originally detailed to be left behind to form a garrison in Lisbon but young Major Stanhope had inherited the persuasive directness of his half-sister and had so pleaded the cause of his 'dirty half hundred' that Moore relented.

Drawing a sheet of hot-pressed paper towards him he wrote swiftly in his thin trailing script. Poor Hester. She hoped for so much more from their relationship than he was able to give. In his heart there was room for only one . . . But her friendship was dear to him and Moore, as she habitually called him, did not forget the warm hospitality of former days when she had reigned supreme as Pitt's hostess.

Now only a trickle of callers elected to leave cards at the modest bow-fronted house near Baker Street where once they might have called in droves. Financial straits bred loneliness, a situation new to one of Hester's opinionated and sociable nature, and one with which she was ill equipped to cope. He therefore ended his letter to her on a companionable note, but could not help confiding his innermost fear.

Pray for good weather, he wrote. If it rains the torrents will swell and be impassable, and I shall be accounted a bungler.

*   *   *

The resort of Paço d' Arcos was a favourite sea-bathing place upon the Tagus some miles from Queluz. The lavish villas of the wealthy were an exclusive coterie high on the cliffs. The village itself comprised a scattering of lime-washed cottages with a humble church dominating a graveyard of lichened tombstones. Beyond the outskirts a chestnut wood extended to a rocky outcrop overlooking the great plain of the bull-breeding region. The skies were autumn clear and the countryside ablaze with colour and the pleasing scent of wild raspberries.

It reminded James Drummond of the coastal hamlets of his native Scotland. The *feira*, pitched just inside the village, was, however, like nothing in his experience.

The cobbled street was swarming with cattle and pigs being prodded marketwards. Women outnumbered the men by ten to one, striding out purposefully with great hampers on their heads containing bread, rice, peas and beans which they offered for sale direct to any who cared to buy, pocketing the proceeds in the recesses of their coarse yellow petticoats. Fish was another commodity widely on sale and what with the pigs and the powerful aroma from the local cheese the air was undeniably heady.

Under the trees near the churchyard, stalls had been set up offering a wide selection of knives, spurs, gold chains, crosses and ear-rings. Red-legged partridges, a local delicacy, hung by their claws from the lower branches awaiting purchase. Children played tag round the ancient stone cross in front of the church and stray dogs wandered through the mêlée adding their excited barking to the general din.

A young dragoon of Jamie's troop was gawping at the antics of a local strong-man, in company with some of his comrades. Kit immediately commandeered him to run his eye over the local horesflesh, for it was an accepted fact that Private Flower had a way with horses, and though in some respects still wet behind the ears as the grass of his local Somerset, there would be no danger of the major being choused.

Dindie lingered at the tempting stalls, begging Jamie, with bubbling enthusiasm, to look at this, that and the other. There was the usual welter of leather goods, woollens, cloth and coarse pottery. At many of the booths the press of people was too great for her to see anything but she succeeded in purchasing four pairs of worsted half-stockings for Kit. She did not dare expend his hard-earned fourteen shillings a day upon any further trifles.

From the other side of the booth Private Daniel Flannigan watched her walk away on the arm of his captain. Officers! He spat venomously. So that was Fane's missus! His thin lip curled.

"Hardly old enough to tie her garters," someone joked.

"She's old enough!" Flannigan grinned knowingly. "Fane knows what he's about. Wouldn't mind a few hours with her meself. Faith, an' I'd be showin' her a trick or two that her fine Major don't know!"

"That's a wicked thing to be saying, Mr Flannigan!" Gabriel Flower joined them, flushed with indignation. "Mrs Fane is a fine lady. 'T'int right for you to be talkin' so disrespec'ful."

"You belt your bloody bone-box! Is it maybe jealous you are, boy?" Flannigan's mouth twisted in a leer. "Why, 'tis a babe we have, to be sure! I'll wager you've not even been near a woman yet. Look at 'im, lads! Sure, the craithur's blushin' like a maid."

"Dammit, Flannigan, you leave the lad alone!"

Corporal Tom Jackson pushed his way to the forefront of the small group and planted himself squarely between the Irishman and his young victim. "I've warned you before to mind your filthy tongue!"

"If it's not Sir Galahad himself! And him coming up so light we nivver heard him. Would you be afther putting me on another charge, Corporal, when me an' young Blossom here is just like David an' Jonathan?"

Flannigan's insolent smile flicked over Jackson carelessly but there was venom behind it, none the less. Jackson was everything he hated — intelligent, quiet-spoken, keen to get on in the Army yet with an underlying toughness which it did not pay to underestimate. Jackson was staring him out with deliberate calm. Flannigan spat derisively and strolled off without a backward glance. Two bloody dog-legs on his arm and he fancied himself God Almighty! He would get that bastard Jackson yet but in his own time. He flung himself down on a grassy bank and began to whistle noisily.

"If you want to catch the dancing, Dindie, you had best come now!"

Flushed with elation Kit took his wife's arm. He had paid one hundred and fifty dollars for a sturdy bay mare and laid out another hundred on a little black pony for Dindie. After much deliberation young Flower had eventually agreed that the animals were in good condition, as prime bits of Blood as would be found anywhere.

"May I not see the new horses first, Kit?"

"No, we shall miss half the fun if we go back. They are performing what is called *flamenco*. You must see it!"

There was a burning light in his eyes which puzzled Dindie, for his attitude towards the fair had not been one of bounding enthusiasm. However, she too wanted to see the gypsy dancers. Her new pony must wait.

It seemed that the entire concentration of British troops had elected to congregate at Paço d' Arcos that day. There was barely a space in the jostling, whistling circle of spectators not occupied by a red or blue coat of some description.

The gypsy troupe hailed from Spanish Andalusia. Swarthy moustachioed guitar players accompanied the dancers and the music itself was raw, turbulent, emotional. Unexpectedly the tempo changed and a single couple took the grassy stage, the man lithe, small-hipped, the girl . . .

The girl was beautiful, vibrant as fire. She wore a flame-coloured gown which hugged her body's every curve like a second skin and her mane of black hair tossed seductively as she glided with feline grace in the arms of her partner, the sun dazzling brilliantly on her multi-bangled wrists and the gold of her ear-rings.

Dindie watched, transfixed by the nubile expressiveness of the girl's body. She played with her partner, encouraged him — was coy, then shocked, tossing away her head while he hung over her, now throwing herself quite back in his arms, her head hanging down as if lifeless. At the quickening urgency of the music his hand clasped her waist and they glided once more as

62

one, she pressing close to him in the most sensitive points of contact.

Dindie could clearly distinguish the girl's face — flushed, the olive skin satin smooth, dark eyes responding exultantly to the guitar's torrid acceleration. The pair had now moved close to where she stood with Kit. Dindie cast a sidelong glance at her husband, curious to discover what he thought of the spectacle.

Kit's eyes were upon the gypsy girl, his mouth parted slightly. It was plain from her bold glance that the girl was aware of his admiration, even returned it. Kit, with his striking blond looks, stood out in any crowd. Dindie's heart contracted. In that instant she knew a quickening of fear.

The girl was now so close that an arm's length might allow contact. With a crashing chord the *bolero* exploded into a climax of snapping castanets, heel-stamping and flourished petticoats. At the peak of her frenzied performance the girl spun from her partner's side and sank to her knees before Kit with a throaty laugh.

Her silken black hair was fallen over her face, yet not enough to obscure the blatant invitation behind the lowered lashes. With a careless flick she tossed him the flower from her hair. He caught it neatly and Dindie winced to see the deliberation with which he crushed the scented petals between his fingers and the cool acknowledgment in his smile.

As the final strum of the guitars died under thunderous cheers the girl rose gracefully and ran to join her partner, greeting the deafening applause with a blown kiss.

Dindie felt Jamie's hand on her elbow. Bemusedly she smiled up at him, although never in her life had she felt less like doing so.

"She is quite beautiful, do not you think?" she whispered.

"She's nocht but a hussy!" he answered brusquely.

Dindie hugged the worsted stockings to her as though they were a talisman. 'La Pasionaria.' The Passion Flower . . . The girl was well billed. She turned to speak to Kit but he was no longer by her side.

Jamie answered her unspoken question. "He's gone to collect the new horses, I think. We might as well take another look at the acrobats."

Dindie allowed him to lead her firmly back to the bustling crush of the *feira*. Kit would be back soon. Her fears were groundless.

Jamie knew otherwise. He had already witnessed Private Flower take the road back to Belem some time earlier with the major's beasts in tow. He also knew that Kit was even now disappeared into the dappled interior of the chestnut woods and that he had not gone alone.

5

Santarém was left behind, an unpretentious hotch-potch of towers and rooftops basking on a ridge commanding the vast, humid plains of the bull-breeding Ribatejo. James Drummond drank in the mellow beauty, wishing he might capture it for ever on canvas. At his right hand the gradient fell sharply away, descending through olive groves to the valley of the Tagus. At this point the river flowed wide, winding past stubble fields of harvested wheat and pasture meadows where the grass was so thick it appeared blue, with smoke-wreathed villages smelling strongly of bull drowsing on the marshy banks.

It seemed to Jamie there was almost a Celtic charm to this fertile lowland of Portugal. October blackberries glistened over rough stone walls beside the road, old women in pattens tended smallholdings boasting only a solitary cow or pig, red-legged partridges and quail flew above the olive trees and at every turn bright drifts of buttercup, periwinkle and rock-rose opened exultantly to the warm sun that played on his face as he rode.

Before and behind him the squadron stretched in a snaking blue column of jangling bridles. They had quit the barracks at Belem three days now. It was good to be on the move, to have a purpose. Even more satisfying was the fact that his troop had been one of the two chosen to make up the commander-in-chief's cavalry escort. General Moore had remained in Lisbon with his staff until the bulk of the army was safely on the advance by its four diverging routes. He was now hastening to catch up his infantry to lead the stab into enemy territory. Already the squadron had overtaken the baggage and ammunition waggons with the scores of women and children trudging along in their wake. A snatch of song drifted back from the blue ranks in front —

> For a soldier I listed
> To grow great in fame
> And be shot at for sixpence a day . . .

A wry smile tugged at Jamie's mouth. The essence of soldiering in a nutshell. The catchy tune remained with him, lightening the monotony of the march.

"Reckon we be halting soon, Corporal Jackson? Sally here has cast a shoe an' she be creatin' something cruel."

"See the farrier-sergeant when we reach Golegā, Flower. We'll not halt more than five minutes at the next stop."

"Oh, I knows how to cold-shoe her," returned Gabriel Flower, with the supreme confidence of his eighteen years. " 'T'int no trouble. Only them stones be so sharp, like."

"If you are able to fix her yourself, so much the better. Apply to Captain Drummond for a ticket to fall out and make certain you catch up the troop at our next halt."

"I'll do that, Corporal." Flower gave Sally an encouraging pat. Not only was he anxious to have her shod, he found himself extremely hungry. A stretch-out on the grass with a lump of cold beef on ration biscuit and a swig from his canteen to wash it down . . . Not that he cared much for grog but the dusty miles made for keen appetites and the grey dawn at which the march commenced seemed a million years away.

It was trumpets, curses, roll up blankets, assemble at the alarm-post, form in close column, 'By sections of threes, march!' Sometimes Flower wondered if the British Army didn't do more foot-slogging than anything else.

Just then the halt was sounded. Jamie spurred his horse and galloped back along the line of march, passing the ponderous train of baggage and thanking his stars he was not responsible for prodding on the recalcitrant mules and bullocks, none of which understood English words of command. Many of the locally recruited muleteers had deserted soon after leaving Lisbon and as the Army's meat ration also travelled 'on the hoof' the resulting chaos on the narrow roads would have required a rearguard of angels to keep tempers from fraying.

Captain Drummond was by no means displeased, however, that the general's party had met up the Baggage. It afforded him the opportunity to exchange a word with young Mrs Fane. Next to Kit he was come to regard Dindie as being his especial property and experienced a pang of resentment whenever he found her being monopolised by the young blades on Moore's staff.

He could not readily explain this attitude. It was not simply the social gap separating those high-born officers and himself. Jamie had the good sense not to be ashamed of his humble background. His father was a churchman, who had taught him to scorn pretention and cant. If an answer to this upsurge of possessiveness did occur to nettle Jamie's quiet moments he took pains to dismiss it firmly from his thoughts.

He found Dindie seated with some soldiers' wives, evidently delighting in renewing their acquaintanceship. Across her lap a baby cooed face downward, whilst she swathed its lower reaches with a fresh napkin under the supervision of its mother. At sight of Jamie she kissed the infant's downy head and returned him to his Mama's breast.

"Jamie! How nice." She came towards him dimpling ruefully. "Has Kit sent you to check up on me?"

"He likes me to keep an eye on you when he's busy," returned James Drummond severely. "It's hardly the same thing. Have you eaten yet?"

She shrugged. "I shall have something later."

"That means you've been giving away half your rations to Paddy O'Flynn's bairns. If Kit finds out he'll not be pleased."

"But you will not tell him, Jamie." The brown eyes laughed up at him with that coaxing insistence which never failed to trigger a response within him. At the mention of her husband, however, the gaiety left her face. Jamie frowned. He had long suspected that all was not well between her and Kit. It disturbed him, though the situation was hardly a surprise — Kit had rushed headlong into this marriage expecting to carry on his life style as before, giving barely a thought for his responsibilities to this loyal, uncomplaining young cousin who so obviously adored him. That, thought Jamie angrily, was the sin of it. For all the attention Kit paid to her she might be part of his horse-furniture or a fly on the wall.

And it showed. In her eyes, wistful for his approach at the end of the day, when the officers congregated in small messes to cook dinner. A careless tweaking of her side-curls, a brief word or two — as one might take notice of a pet dog — then she would be left to her own devices whilst Kit embarked on a game of faro or joined the commander-in-chief at dinner.

Of course she was a great favourite with all ranks, never without an attendance of subalterns anxious to secure for her the best seat by the camp-fire, the tastiest morsel at mealtimes. Her youth, unworldly innocence and cheerful acceptance of personal discomfort earned her willing slaves. Her black pony was frequently escorted surreptitiously by more than one private and she delighted in their friendly overtures, accepting the hastily plucked wild flowers and berries they offered, making them repeat the words of their favourite songs and begging to learn about their families back in England.

It was plain Kit approved of his young wife shaping so well. When she made some naïve remark which struck his friends as amusing, when he saw them vying to sit next her and answer her ceaseless questions, his approving glance would find her — transforming her countenance at a stroke.

One warm glance, one genuine demonstration of affection . . . was it so much to expect? Jamie glanced down into the wistful young face, a rush of frustration possessing him. Kit ought to have insisted she travel with the Baggage column, like the other wives, instead of forcing her to keep pace with the squadron. With the women at least she might forget her loneliness. Confound Kit! And confound that Spanish whore who had followed them from Lisbon.

He could see the gypsy girl perched brazenly on the pole draught of a hooped commissary waggon. Her raven hair hung loose and her skirts were arranged to flagrantly expose her legs to the press of leering soldiers who fought to get near. As Jamie watched she flicked a *cigarro* from the lips of one private and inhaled, blowing the smoke into his eyes with a bold laugh. Jamie turned grimly away. A trollop if ever he saw one. He glanced sidelong at Dindie wondering what she was thinking. Her gaze was fixed straight ahead as though oblivious to the girl's coquetry, but beneath its faint tan her face looked strained.

The bugle call 'To Horse' signalled an end of their brief halt. Jamie walked Mrs Fane back to her tethered pony and helped her mount.

"You will not tell Kit . . . about the rations?" she repeated, as though glad of something to say.

"I'd never cause trouble for you — you know that," retorted Jamie bluntly.

Dindie watched him stride off, wanting to call him back yet hesitant. His warm understanding was her shield against Kit's indifference. To him she might talk naturally without fear of disgracing herself by some social gaffe. It was her abiding dread, this horror of making Kit a subject of ridicule through some thoughtless act or word. The general's 'family' now included two recent additions, zealous Henry Hardinge and seventeen-year-old Harry Burrard, son of their bumbling former second-in-command, who was become badly smitten with her, much to Kit's amusement. They were all without exception country gentlemen or the sons of peers, yet though they treated her with kindness and unfailing courtesy Dindie could not shake off her inhibitions.

It was natural, she supposed, that Kit should discourage her involvement with the wives of the dragoons. Dindie tried to argue that it was easier for her to identify with them than with his blasé, Eton-educated comrades.

"You forget I was brought up the daughter of a country doctor, Kit. I have never been used to mixing with persons of rank, excepting Aunt Auden and yourself. But I do feel for women such as Mrs Baillie and Sadie O'Flynn! Why, in Dean there was no distinction — Papa involved himself with his patients as a friend, not simply when they were sick or in need of time to pay."

"That is well enough, Dindie, but Army etiquette demands a wholly different approach. I will not allow you to become coarsened by mixing with these women as the fancy takes you. Your mother was a lady and so are you! Do you understand?"

Dindie stifled a sigh. Always they seemed to end up arguing. She saw so little of Kit during the day. Even now, riding in close proximity, their exchanges were brief for Kit rode with the general and Colonel Graham, taking it for granted that her pony would keep up and knowing that with Jamie she was in safe hands. Only in the early hours before dawn broke did Dindie feel that her husband truly belonged to her. The warm intimacy, the roughness of his chin pressing into her breast as he slept aroused in her odd pangs of longing deep inside that she did not fully understand. In the half light of morning she might lay her hand against his heart, her arms enfold him without inhibition, her lips brush his skin. All this she might do because Kit was deep in sleep and unaware.

Wistfully she assured herself that he did care, that she must cease minding if he did not actually tell her so. He is not sorry that he married you, she reminded herself, blinking back tears. He said so . . .

She watched Mrs O'Flynn get a leg-up aboard a tarpaulined waggon from her husband and felt a twinge of envy. However lowly her station Sadie's marriage was solid. I cannot claim as much, thought Dindie unhappily.

*   *   *

They bivouacked that night at Abrantes in the shadow of the mountains, having crossed the Tagus by ferry-boats. General Moore had decided to halt there in conjunction with his rearguard, for the road now wound upwards through sombre, hostile-looking country which promised to prove taxing on the horses. It was his intention to press on at daybreak with his staff, for he had decided upon Salamanca as the junction for his armies and he must be on hand to meet the troops as they arrived.

Dindie felt relief that the threatening rains had so far held off else they would have been obliged to billet themselves in the dirty hovels where the doorways were so low that the inhabitants were forced to bend double in order to go out and in.

Bivouacking in the open was still an adventure to her. They made camp on the edge of a wood close by the river and whilst the troops went to draw water and rations the women washed clothes in the swirling shallows. This was an evening ritual observed whenever possible by every soldier's wife; after the grimy sweat of the march it was the only opportunity of securing a change of clean linen for themselves and their menfolk. Officers' ladies were naturally exempt from such a task. The wives of the Patlanders were the self-appointed washerwomen of the Army and Kit had already engaged the wife of one of the sergeants in the 18th to wait upon Dindie, although after one session of allowing his shirts and under-linen to the well-meaning attentions of Mrs McCluskey, Dindie itched to scrub them herself.

Instead, she walked into a village on the outskirts of Abrantes to buy bread. The loaves throughout this region of Portugal tasted sour and were generally full of sand from the soft millstones, but even this did not prevent the sharp-eyed vendors from charging the enormous price of a shilling a pound. Any bread was preferable to the jaw-breaking ships' biscuit or the black 'Tommy' regulation issue, which was so thick it would stick to a wall like paste. This item was a continual source of grievance amongst the men. They argued with justification that even paupers and felons were allowed white bread and roundly cursed the Horse Guards for their stinginess.

Upon her return Dindie found pickets posted and arms piled, and the wood resounding to the chopping of boughs and branches

71

whilst fires already lit were heating the heavy iron camp-kettles. Kit's batman had constructed a barricade of saddles and baggage for warmth and was now arranging blankets over a matress of boughs for her to lie upon. This makeshift couch, though hardly comfortable, was a necessary precaution against the imminent drenching downpours. Bedding down on the bare earth, they had been warned, could mean awaking chin deep in a morass of mud.

"Flannigan, you'll water your mount and get her to the forge-cart before you think of your own belly!"

Corporal Tom Jackson straightened from unsaddling his chestnut stallion. If there was one thing he despised it was a trooper who failed to care for his horse first and foremost. If he knew anything of Flannigan the Irishman's mount would be neither groomed, watered nor fed until the wretched beast lashed out in desperation. Well, my lad, thought Jackson grimly, this time will be different.

Purposely he strode to Flannigan's horse and lifted up its tail. "Call this groomed, do you?" he rasped angrily. "Look at her, man! Don't you know how to handle a dock-sponge?"

"Be jabers, Corporal, is it me that's at fault if me poor old screw evacuates her bowels like she's got the runs?"

Flannigan stood his ground defiantly, baiting mockery in his eyes. "B'Jasus, boys, if the man's not hisself. Mebbe it's his darlin' wife he's missing them cold nights." His grin changed to a leer. "Is it worried yez are, Corporal, 'bout what she's doin' back in England — and mebbe who she's doin' it with?"

"You snivelling bloody Mick! I'll teach you to rinse out your mouth!"

Jackson's breath came heavily. Grasping the slightly built Irishman by the stable-jacket he lifted him contemptuously, bundling him headlong before him. In the struggle Flannigan slipped and fell heavily into the copious excrement left by his horse.

"Don't *ever* soil my wife's name with your cowardly lies!"

72

gritted Jackson, white-faced. "Horse dung's too bloody good for the likes of you, Flannigan!"

He watched the private's attempts to get out of the reeking filth with quiet satisfaction. A grinning, jeering audience had congregated. Serve the creature right to be made a laughing-stock for once! He wished he might have split open that sneering weasel face but to do so would have played into Flannigan's hands. Jackson had not earned his stripes to lose them so readily on account of a rat like Dan Flannigan.

Anger subsiding, he rubbed down his horse and filled a bucket with hay, thinking the while of his young wife Mary back in their poky little rooms in Whitechapel. God, how he missed her, longed for the warmth of her pressed close, the tumble of auburn hair tickling his chin, spilling over her bare shoulders . . .Like an angel she was, the sweetest-natured creature and her eyes — there never were such eyes, speckled greenish-brown, cool and mysterious as a trout stream. They had saved hard to get married and now, just when they had made their home snug and neat and were thinking of starting a family, the regiment was ordered on foreign service.

Jackson closed his eyes tightly. She was already too thin, too wasted. And as always when he faced that fact an unmentionable fear gripped his insides. She told him he was not to worry — everyone became peaky this end of the year. She would eat proper, and there was the bit of money that her sewing brought in.

Jackson felt a prick of tears starting. Resolutely he turned his attention to his horse.

*   *   *

By clubbing together their various rations the junior officers of Moore's staff succeeded in producing a tolerable dinner. The addition of a hare which George Napier had obtained from a local peasant by outright bribery was judged a capital bonus and when the *vinho da casa* of the environs of Abrantes proved undrinkable, Percy suggested augmenting their slim reserves of brandy with spirits of wine from the hospital stores, an experiment which generated such hiccup and happiness that their small mess was soon joined round the fire by the commander-in-chief.

"I give you the subalterns' toast — 'A bloody war on a sickly season!' " Harry Percy crashed his tin mug against a stone and laughed at Dindie's perplexed expression. "It's like this, Mrs Fane. Every four-button Johnny knows his surest chance of promotion without purchase comes by stepping into a dead man's shoes. It sounds singularly cold-blooded," he added, kindly, "but who wants to end up a forty-year-old ensign?"

Dindie shivered. "Is the casualty rate very high?"

"Not high enough," declared Percy cheerfully, bestowing Kit a wicked grin. "Above the rank of major they cling to life with wonderful tenacity. 'Course, one's chance of promotion is virtually assured if the regiment is posted to some God-awful station like the West Indies or New South Wales. Yellow Jack picks 'em off like flies."

"That is enough of such talk, Harry," reproved his chief, who had been listening quietly and seen Dindie's colour change. He regarded her with his grave smile.

"Have no fear, Mrs Fane. Your major is the very devil of a fellow but he takes uncommon good care of his skin."

Dindie's heart glowed at this intervening tact. Already she was attracted, despite herself, to the general's likeable personality. Since the commencement of the advance he had shown himself concerned for her well-being, taking a father-like interest which both touched and pleased her, for she knew him to be preoccupied with countless matters of grave importance. Kit had confided the chief's unease at this risky separation of his forces. Without cavalry support in numbers the infantry was dangerously vulnerable to attack, yet on the soundest authority assurances had been given that only the route through Madrid was suitable for cavalry and artillery. The weather was uncertain, there was not a decent map to be had and now, to add to Moore's frustration, it was daily becoming evident that he had been misinformed about the mountain roads and he might, after all, have kept his infantry screened.

George Napier poured a measure of the brandy punch into Dindie's mug and added hot water and a spoonful of their precious sugar ration. "There, Mrs Fane! Get that down you and I guarantee you shan't feel the cold."

Dindie looked doubtfully at the drink and then at Kit. He nodded for her to try it. She took a sip and was astonished at the fiery warmth which engulfed her insides. The sugar diminished the bitterness of the mixture and the warm glow tingled pleasantly to her toes.

"I like it," she pronounced, taking another sip.

Napier smiled triumphantly. "Told you so. We shall make a soldier of you yet. I say, sir, what about a chorus? We're regular nightingales at 'Brighton Camp' and 'Britons, strike home', ain't we, fellows?"

Moore rose, shaking his head. "I had as lief hear the braying of our friends the pack-mules," he smiled. "And I suspect Colonel Graham and my excellent quartermaster-general feel likewise." He winked at General George Murray as he spoke. "And I have correspondence to answer, besides."

"Me, too." Kit rose in mock horror. "I mean to take a turn about camp."

Dindie watched him stride off under a tirade of good-natured abuse in the wake of Moore and General Murray. How she wished she might accompany him but he had not asked her. She warmed her hands round the hot mug and drank deeply. The night air was sharp. Even with Kit's dolman on above her riding-habit she felt cold. She glanced across at Jamie and smiled, glad that Kit had included him in their circle, yet aching with sympathy over the uncomfortableness which she suspected he must be suffering. Quietly she slipped to his side, encouraging him with a warm handclasp to join in the lusty singing.

By a neighbouring camp-fire Private Flannigan sat with his cronies from C Troop listening to the hearty voices raised in song. Staff officers! He spat roundly. They could afford to sing, with them fancy accents and well-filled bellies. Not that he'd done so bad for himself, thieving a fat turkey from a farm down the road. He drew heavily on his pipe. Now they were attacking his favourite, murdering it, he thought sourly. 'Savourneen Deelish' . . . dearest darling. The melancholy Irish air turned his reflections unaccountably to Moll Sullivan.

He wondered if she'd had his brat yet. The hell with it — he was well shot of her. But for Moll Sullivan he wouldn't be in this God-forsaken hole, wouldn't be in the bloody Army in the first place! He had fallen prey to the recruiting sergeant in a Dublin alehouse. Oh, he'd been easy meat, sure enough, running from the law and hungry. But there had been Moll Sullivan seven months gone and her father and brothers threatening to spread the road with his insides if he didn't get her to a priest quick.

Flannigan smiled to himself at the remembrance. Get tied down on account of a brat? Not he. He could have slipped the Sullivans easy. Tinkers they were, miserable bloody tinkers. Moll had been all right though — he was sorry leaving her with a squealer on the way, but if it hadn't been him she'd have got done by some other bloke.

He wouldn't mind a turn with that flighty Spanish bit, though. Paquita, that was her name or something like. Wouldn't take him long to get over the garters there. Flannigan stared morosely into the leaping flames. God, he still smelt of horse! It clung to his nostrils, to his overalls, every damned bit of him. His mouth twisted cruelly. This time, Jackson, he vowed, I'll even the score proper.

Private Flower was on picket duty some miles to the front. The moon shed an ominous light, gilding tree and outcrop with an eerie menace. Proper creepy, it were. Every sound carried miles on the still air. It was rumoured they might soon be meeting up with the French. Flower fervently hoped the enemy would delay their visit one night more. What did a Frenchman look like, anyroads? He pondered the thought as he patrolled the lonely stretch of farmland allocated to him.

He had never thought much about an actual encounter with the

Frog. How would it be, he wondered uneasily, to be faced with killing a fellow human being in the heat of battle? To slash down one's sabre as a ploughboy cuts down nettles with a stick . . . A good blow would take a man's head off, he knew. It had been impressed upon them often enough at sword drill. But to actually *do* it — that was different. A sweat stood out on his brow and he found himself trembling.

Kit breathed the night air appreciatively. After a long day in the saddle it was good to stretch one's legs. He sought out his baggage mule and unstrapped his oilskin. The covering would afford Dindie some additional warmth. Her pluck both surprised and delighted him. Not once had she murmured at their rough and ready existence or at the scant privacy. It would be her seventeenth birthday in about six weeks. I shall buy her some special frippery, he decided. Ciudad Rodrigo and Salamanca were both large cities. Presumably he would find something suitable there. The idea of surprising her rather appealed to him and it was with a light step he returned to the group by the camp-fire.

The mirth and song were still in progress. With a stab of shock he realised it was Dindie who was providing both. She was perched on a mound of piled knapsacks gaily obliging her appreciative audience with some ditty or other. There was much laughter and encouragement. Her impromptu solo was evidently going down well with every man present except Jamie, who sat glaring like a latterday Calvin.

Espying his approach Dindie's face broke into a radiant smile. The brandy had made her feel deliciously warm and carefree. She no longer felt unsure amongst these young officers, and now Kit was returned and would be proud to see her entering so well into the spirit of things.

With renewed vigour her voice embarked on a catchy arrangement, a favourite she had learned on the march.

> Our grandfather's name was Sir Adam,
> Who managed the king's nursery ground,

And was getting on well until Madam
Stealing pippins one morning was found.

The ladies they say have odd fancies,
But so have the gentlemen too.
I can guess pretty well what is Nancy's,
'Tis one that she never shall —

"Dindie!" The shocked interruption hissed like a bullet, startling her into silence. What had she done? What had he to be so
furious about?

"Go over there and wait for me!" breathed Kit, so beside
himself he could barely speak. Rounding on her audience he said
coldly, "The spectacle is over, gentlemen! I only trust you are
proud of yourselves, allowing my wife to make sport for you
all!"

"Steady on, old man — it's not how you think!"

George Napier leaped to his feet in protest. "She wanted to sing.
We never dreamed she'd — "

"How much of that accursed brandy has she drunk?" demanded
Kit, furiously. "Do you consider it amusing to allow Dindie to get
tipsy for your gratification? Do you?" His eyes blazed. "I should
like to knock you down for this night's work, Napier."

"Kit, she's not tipsy — not much, anyway."

Jamie intervened quietly, taking his friend to one side before he
did anything he might regret. "She did drink too much of the stuff
but no one pressed it upon her, I swear. I think maybe she felt
despondent, or it might be she was simply cold." He caught at
Kit's arm. "Don't be too harsh with her. It's not her fault."

"I ought never to have left her!" muttered Kit, grim-faced. He
stared hard at Jamie, then turned on his heel.

Dindie looked up timidly at his approach. She was left no time to
plead her cause.

"Where did you learn the words of that vulgar song?" he
demanded. "Who taught it to you?"

"I . . . I have heard the men sing it," she whispered. "I did not realise it was v-vulgar. Truly, Kit!"

"Well, it is. *Excessively!*" He hoped to God she did not understand the crudities of the following two verses. Flinging himself down upon his blankets he said, tight-lipped, "You had best get to sleep. It's late."

*   *   *

Dindie lay huddled in her blankets, studying the pattern of stars in the black night. Even with all her clothes on she felt cold. Black objects moved against the camp-fires' glare. Noises reached her — soldiers talking quietly over a last pipe of tobacco, the raucous croak of frogs from the river, a bullock's mournful lowing. Her eyes, wet-lashed with tears, fastened on Kit lying next to her. He was restless. She felt him turn, heard his soft curse as the branches bit into his flesh. She had made him look a fool, disgraced him in front of his fellows . . .

Clutching a damp handkerchief to her breast she whispered chokily, "Kit . . . I — I'm sorry."

He did not answer but his arm reached out to cover her body. Dindie snuggled close, creeping her hand into his, the night chill banished in the warmth of that forgiving gesture.

Kit lay for some time listening to the night sounds. He felt Dindie turn sleepily into his shoulder. Very gently he eased his body free and stood up, covering her with his boat-cloak, then quietly made his way by the glow of the fires to the perimeter of the camp where the dark trees swayed like mournful ghosts.

"All clear, Jackson?"

"Quiet as the grave, sir. Vedettes report no sign of the enemy in the immediate area."

Kit gave a satisfied nod then asked, as an afterthought, "Mrs Fane tells me your wife has been sick?"

"Yes, sir." Jackson spoke tightly. "Wanted to come out with us she did, but I says no — never been strong, my Mary has. But . . . there's more to it, Major. I just know there is." In the darkness his voice held an edge of despair. "I've seen it afore — starts with a cough, just like hers . . . She's real sick, sir."

Kit detected the choked-down emotion and frowned. Consumption, most probably, the scourge of the working class. Wretched housing and lack of nourishing food — twin evils old as time. He wished there was some way to help. Jackson was a good sort, not the usual scum which flocked to the Colours. A worried soldier did not make a good soldier. For once he was grateful that Dindie's artless questioning had alerted him to the corporal's state of mind.

"I was wondering, Major, if maybe there was a means of sending Mary a bit from my pay, when it comes through. If I could even get a few shillings to her she'd be able to eat proper. It's what she needs — if she's ever to get strong."

Kit remained doubtful. What Jackson's wife required was to get out of London, to breathe pure country air and enjoy a regular diet. Kate or George could doubtless use an extra hand to tackle plain-sewing. He knew their mother might be relied upon to arrange matters.

"I shall raise the matter with Paymaster Burke in the morning, Jackson. And don't worry, man. We'll work something out."

Kit acknowledged the obedient salute and moved off into the shadow of the trees, deep in thought. A twig snapped close by and in the shaft of moonlight a figure emerged from behind one of the supply waggons.

The girl stood waiting, one arm resting leisurely on her hip. Kit hesitated then strode forward and drew her silently into his arms, feeling a rising excitement fire through him.

"Paquita, this is wrong," he murmured huskily. "You know very well we ought not to be — " Her breath rose on the cold air, the warm scent of her tantalising his nostrils. "*Malo — depravado!*" Crushing her to him he abandoned further protest and kissed her savagely.

"*Ah, tu hermoso! Me gusto mucho.*"

Laughing softly she placed a finger against his lips and drew him swiftly down with her till they melted into the black night.

6

THE WEATHER BROKE on November 6th. At first the thunder rolling ominously in the peaks had seemed like distant gunfire but then came the rain — drenching, incessant, the black clouds bursting overhead as though in savage delight.

Even the beauty of the mountain country through which the troops passed could not lessen the misery. Seen through driving rain and barely distinguishable for mist, towns and villages bearing marvellously resonant Portuguese names became synonymous with mud-walled billets shared with the poorest of hosts. In her diary Dindie recorded humble meals of brown bread dipped in olive oil, night after night of trying to sleep on bare floors in company with the family, the family cow and goat and in many instances a visiting rat or two; of being poisoned by noxious fumes from the inevitable fire of cow-dung in the middle of the room and being eaten alive by fleas — the only inhabitants certain to bestow a personal welcome.

Vila-Velha, Castelo Branco, Alpendrinha, Monsanto. Names which tripped off the tongue, and which in summer must be unquestionably beautiful, nestling amidst cork forests or by a rushing torrent but which for Dindie would always be associated with blackened hovels and poverty-stricken peasants, invariably hospitable and always unwashed.

Thankfully, there were lighter moments to record, often accompanied in the margin by a lightning sketch with one of the newly-invented pencils which Kit kept by him for writing in the field. A mountain shepherd in peculiar cloak fashioned out of straw, a trio of eagles watching silently from a high crag. And who could forget tasting *geropiga*, a distinctive local wine chased down with roasted chestnuts? Or seeing cheese being made from ewe's milk in wooden troughs? Best of all to Dindie's mind had been hearing the wild mysterious *cantorias por cantorias* — greetings called between shepherds from one mountain slope to another, and the colourful festival of Our Lady of the Hawthorn in which a small figure of the Saviour dressed in uniform was borne in celebration through the streets.

Now they were high in the gaunt ridges of the Serra da Estrela, following the appalling road over water-rutted tracks so steep and slippery that the horses could not keep their footing. Frequently the general's Portuguese guide lost his way, like so many of the regiments they passed en route, and they would be forced to shelter from the driving sleet behind protective clefts of rock. Dindie lost count of the number of exhausted bullocks and waggon-loads of biscuit and medical supplies stuck fast in the squelching passes. Her own crushing fatigue overwhelmed all else.

The route wound sickeningly over the summits in hairpin bends, icy winds tore through rocky gulleys bringing flakes of snow and when Dindie awoke, stiff-limbed and gasping with cold after a night in the open she found her hair frozen to the ground and Kit was obliged to cut it free. At the frontier town of Guarda every convent was packed with men of the leading regiments intent on wringing out sodden uniforms before immense fires. That night for the first time in over a sennight she slept in a proper bed.

The frontier itself was a surprise, and it was here that Dindie's strength finally failed her. As the icy sleet intensified she had fought to keep up, stay awake, guide her tired pony as best she might but her eyes were glazing and her hands so cold she could barely feel the reins. In her distress she cried out to Kit. He was by her side in an instant, swearing furiously at the blizzard which drove into their faces.

"Come, wifeling." She felt herself swung high in his arms. Involuntarily, she clung to him, her breath catching on a sob, then he had set her before him across the saddle, shouting to a dragoon to see to her pony. She was conscious of his strong heartbeat as he held her fast in the crook of one arm.

"That's better?" His chin rested briefly against her hair. Dindie tried to reply but her lashes were already drooping. Reaching up a hand she laid her palm gently on his cheek then her head dropped insensible against his breast.

She awoke to hearty laughter and exclamation. Bemusedly she looked about her and then at Kit. The storm was calmed and they were reined in by a tiny rivulet, so narrow that the dragoons were bestriding it with ease. Kit swung her down from his horse and asked teasingly, "Well, wifeling, what do you think of Spain?"

She stared at him blankly. "Are we in Spain?"

"Your left foot is," he explained, with a smile. "But if you choose to place the other foot *so* —" He straddled the stream as he spoke, "you now have one foot in each country!"

She experimented, delighting in the absurdity. They looked at each other and laughed. Dindie's spirits rose. Before them lay a new country, a fresh beginning. As Kit helped her to remount he stayed one hand fractionally.

"You have coped amazingly well, Dindie," he said softly.

"Did you suppose I could not?" she returned, indignant, yet her heart fluttered with absurd pleasure at his praise.

The difference between the two countries was immediate. Spain was everywhere cleaner, more prosperous, but with each mile of dropping down to the sandy Salamanca plain it became clear that British uniforms were unwelcome. Hostility was rife. Only the Irish seemed guaranteed a degree of hospitality from the Spaniards, being Catholics like themselves. Indolence and touchiness seemed the national characteristics, equalled only by Spanish bragging that Moore's army would be unnecessary. Was not their *valiente* general, the Marqués de la Romana, even now enjoying a hero's welcome at Corunna, having escaped from a French-held garrison in North Germany? Let 'el Senor Napoleon' come!

Suddenly below them, a golden oasis in the plain, lay Salamanca. Seen from the brown hills above it looked, thought Dindie, every inch the unhurried university city, a Spanish Oxford of tawny stone towers cut in two by the River Tormes and joined by a splendid Roman bridge with many arches.

General Moore, suspecting that an elaborate reception committee would be awaiting him and determined to avoid it at all costs, entered the city by dodging down a back road. If there was anything he detested more, he was heard to mutter, it was palaver by well-intentioned but pomp-loving mayors and corporations.

After so many rain-sodden hours and nights in primitive billets the bustling normality of Salamanca's Plaza Mayor lifted Dindie's flagging spirits. Dazzling arcaded shop windows and a delicious aroma of chocolate greeted them as they rode over the cobbles and between high gates fronting the courtyard of a rambling old mansion faced in black-and-white tiles. The Palacio de San Boal was to be Moore's headquarters during their stay, she learned, but her body was so numb with exhaustion that she could not bear even to explore the vast chambers allotted to them.

*   *   *

Bad news greeted the commander-in-chief upon his arrival. The French had taken the city of Burgos and were concentrating in force. The next night a dishevelled courier rode into the courtyard with another despatch. The enemy had entered Valladolid, a mere seventy miles away and within a four-day march of Salamanca.

The situation was perilous. The British force at Salamanca numbered less than 17,000 men with only a single battery of light guns. The French were understood to have crossed the Pyrenees 80,000 strong. If, as seemed likely, the enemy continued their advance Moore would be routed before the hoped-for junction of his armies could be established.

Flanked by his aides and senior generals in the writing-room on the first floor of the Palacio de San Boal, Sir John furrowed his brows over a tattered map heavily inked in with black arrows. The arrows indicated the build-up of enemy strength in the immediate environs.

"Sir John Hope's artillery cannot possibly reach us in time from Madrid and General Baird's force is strung out somewhere in this region . . ." Moore indicated on the map the inhospitable mountain chain between Corunna and Astorga. He spoke briskly but his veiled anxiety was apparent. "It is patently clear our three forces are separated from each other by longer distances than any one of us is from powerful French units."

"What about the Spanish armies?" someone asked.

"What Spanish armies?" muttered Harry Percy to Kit, with rueful emphasis.

It was a pertinent question. The reverses suffered by their Spanish allies had thus far been so catastrophic that it was impossible to guess in what numbers their strength now lay. What little information came from their high command was so grossly exaggerated that it could not be relied on. It was swiftly becoming evident to Moore and his generals that there existed no one Spanish army worthy of the name. A mass of miserable peasantry without clothing, organisation or leadership — and, worst of all, without the will to fight.

It was this dangerous mixture of bombastic confidence and no confidence at all which worried Moore. To a correspondent in Madrid he warned that the Spaniards must not hope to rely on the British presence alone. His Expeditionary Force had been despatched from England to aid the existing Spanish armies but not singly to resist the might of France if the Spaniards themselves made no efforts.

So far there had been little to convince him that such co-operation was at work. Napoleon's crack troops had been enabled to penetrate unscathed and unhindered to within seventy miles of his own slender force, some regiments of which were still battling it out on the rugged storm-lashed roads from Portugal.

Frowning, Moore scanned the map before him, tracing the circuitous route around Madrid which his artillery must take in order to reach Salamanca. He had despatched Graham to the capital some days earlier, for the crushing defeat of the Spaniards at Espinosa and the taking of Burgos had inflamed rumour that Madrid was about to capitulate. It was vital to get at the truth — and quickly.

"But what if the French prevent our junction, General?"

"And the northern column. If we are forced to fall back it risks marching into certain destruction!"

"On the other hand, sir, if General Romana has been appointed as Spanish chief, as rumour has it, there's a sporting chance of his kicking Boney's arse to good effect."

This suggestion from George Napier caused Moore's expression to lose a little of its careworn appearance.

"Until Colonel Graham reports in full I am persuaded to adhere to our original plan, gentlemen. If Hope considers it practical to continue his advance I shall not question his judgment. Meanwhile I shall direct General Baird to collect his corps at Astorga, but not to come towards me until I give him notice."

So saying he resumed his study of the crackling map and the murmurs of discussion continued.

The general's inner disquiet, however, he kept to himself. Despite young Napier's confident assertion, he was growing hourly more convinced of the necessity to retire from Salamanca. Only one Spanish army now remained unbeaten, reputedly fierce and determined but surely no match against Bonaparte's disciplined corps. It was now known that the Emperor himself had crossed the Pyrenees to command his victorious Army in person, a fact calculated only to inflame Moore's frustration still further. Until he heard from Graham, until Hope and Baird reported, until he had some concrete evidence of Spanish solidarity, his hands were tied. And with every hour the French threat drew nearer.

*   *   *

"Looks as though we shall get a crack at the Frog sooner than we thought. It's above time my sabre was notched!"

Dindie heard the burning relish in Napier's voice and turned quickly away, her heart contracting. Resolutely she bent over her darning, shutting her mind to the grim acceleration of events. It was foolish not to accept that at some point they must clash with the enemy but now that the reality was close her blood turned cold. She knew from listening to the veterans of the Helder and Egypt how a man could be hacked to ribbons in seconds. The nightmare tortured her waking moments.

"Their chasseurs are reputed to be damnably crack," mused Kit, studying the evaporating smoke rings from his *cigarro* with thoughtful eyes. "I wonder how it will be?"

At his words silence fell on the knot of aides ranged in varied postures of relaxation about the lofty morning-room. They were all wondering how it would be. The majority of them had never been in action and behind the high spirits and bravado lurked a good deal of trepidation.

"We shall give 'em a dusting, at any rate," declared young Burrard, with determined optimism, returning his attention to the chestnuts he was roasting. "A pox on Boney! If I'm to have my gizzard slit, burn me if I'll not be blind drunk first! I say, Percy, where's that bottle of claret you've been hogging?"

Dindie crept away unnoticed. How could they joke of it so unconcernedly, she shuddered, making her way down the broad staircase. She had taken upon herself the task of stitcher and mender to Kit's friends, and was thankful for the occupation. The immediate future did not bear thinking about . . . and Kit was busy as ever.

But Jamie would be waiting for her. She brightened at the prospect. He had asked her to go shopping with him, explaining with embarrassment that he wanted to purchase some shawls for his mother and sisters, and would she choose for him?

He was waiting just inside the rounded main arch of the courtyard. To her delight she saw that he had engaged a *calesa*.

"Oh, Jamie — you shouldn't have! Why, it's only a step into town. We might easily walk."

"Humbug," he grinned, settling her in the carriage with a rug over her knees. "I've been anticipating this jaunt all day." He sat himself beside her, his gaze lingering on her radiant face. "I really have, Dindie," he added, quietly.

George Napier idly watched Dindie being helped into the light carriage. From his spread-eagled position in the window embrasure he was provided with an excellent view of the main gate. Thoughtfully, he beckoned to Kit.

"If I were you, old man," he murmured, in an undertone, "I should pay Dindie a sight more attention than you do at present. She's a darling, you know. There must be no end of fellows willing to do it for you."

Kit stiffened. "Like yourself, perhaps?"

Napier raised one black eyebrow and motioned towards the courtyard where the *calesa* was turning out of the gate.

"Like a certain young hussar captain, for instance," he responded drily.

"Don't take me for a flat, George. Why, Jamie's my best friend." Irritably, Kit turned away. "I'd trust him with my life."

"But would you trust him with Dindie?" persisted Napier.

"A damned sight liefer than trust her to an experienced rooster such as you!" retorted Kit hotly, ruffled and trying not to show it. Immediately shouts of encouragement broke out.

"You tell him, Major! Those Napiers pinch all the girls. His brother Charles is equally as bad."

"Napier can't help being a flirt. Comes of having King Charles the Second for his great-great-grandfather, even if it was wrong side of the blanket."

"Oh, stuff!" Napier swung his long legs to the floor and grinned at his persecutors. "I'm engaged to dine with the 50th this evening. Now that Charles and Stanhope are running the regiment between 'em they keep a decent table. Who's for joining me?"

Kit left them arguing and went to the quarters he shared with Dindie, a pleasant if imposing set of rooms on the first floor. Her bedchamber door was ajar, the muslin gown she was to wear at dinner laid out in readiness on the counterpane. Kit touched its filmy softness, depression settling upon him. Napier's hint was well-intentioned but misguided, curse him. Well, wasn't it? To Kit's surprise he realised he was experiencing something very like jealousy. He remembered how she had laughed up into Harry Percy's eyes during a waltz at the *tertullia* given by one of the local hidalgos. Every eye had followed their progress for they made a handsome couple circling dashingly . . . Was it any wonder, argued Kit, I should lose my temper with her, flirting with Percy under my nose?

Moodily Kit strode to his own room and flung himself on the canopied bed. A darling, Napier had said. Certainly she was, but he resented being told off for neglect, just the same. He tried to assuage his feelings by assuring himself that Dindie preferred it that way. Hadn't she clawed like a wildcat against his advances that first night together? Any other husband would have taken her long before now. But he had given her his word. Yet the picture remained to vex him of the intimate way her head had bent towards Jamie's, her unconcealed pleasure in his society. Savagely, Kit reached for a book and pretended to read.

*   *   *

"To think this bridge has carried the traffic of almost two thousand years!"

At the awed exclamation from Harry Percy a ripple of amusement lightened the discussion between the party of riders reined in to admire the view. Sir John Moore was snatching an hour from his desk to take a look at Salamanca and the camps outside it.

"The Romans constructed bridges to last, Harry," he smiled, glancing over the parapet. In the still waters of the Tormes the fifteen arches were transposed, with the ochre towers and cupolas, into a giant panoramic reflection. On the banks women were washing clothes in the shallows, their lively chatter carrying audibly to the officers on the bridge.

"I fancy Caesar's staff officers enjoyed the smiles of the local *doncellas* too. See, gentlemen, there is rather a fetching one bidding our young friend *hasta mañana*."

Percy's cheeks burned at the chief's gentle teasing. He rather wished it were possible to get to know the name of his bold admirer, but there was small chance of it this afternoon.

"I suppose there's no accounting for taste, sir," grinned Kit, doffing his cocked staff hat in mock salute to the discomfited Percy, who favoured him with a questionable gesture and a flick back of his sandy hair. Kit smiled appreciatively. Dindie was safe enough with this young dasher. Percy was too much of a butterfly to be content with one blossom for any length of time.

Moore listened to their banter with fatherly indulgence. He thought the world of them, delighting in their burning enthusiasm for life. They kept him young in outlook with their careless slang, their talk of girls and prize-fight heroes. It was Fane and Napier and Percy who shielded the general from endless officials and long-winded grandees. They it was who diplomatically turned conversation at dinner in the Palacio de San Boal when their commander-in-chief's patience looked stretched.

Never one to suffer fools gladly, Moore found that the long hours at his desk were now beginning to tell upon him in a way they never had formerly. He worked a punishing sixteen hours every day, rising at four and lighting his own fire in the vast sleeping apartment while his aides still slept and by the light of candles on his writing-table took up his solitary pen until eight or nine, when he would join them for breakfast. Afterwards, there would be generals to receive and papers to sign and a poring over maps in the long narrow room overlooking the square, units to visit and orders and despatches to issue, then back to his desk and more correspondence.

But worry and sleeplessness were taking their toll. He found himself unusually irritable over trivial matters and his face was grown pale. Colborne had remarked upon it with his accustomed forthrightness and Sir John, with wry humour, put it down to advancing years. He was a few days past his forty-seventh birthday yet, to his acute satisfaction, his physique was if anything more powerful than before. Could Lady Hester Stanhope see him at this moment riding on at the head of his small party she would never have chided him, as she had on one occasion, on the dangers of his developing a stoop. On his cream-coloured charger with its black mane and tail he felt, and indeed looked, every inch the victor-elect.

And yet . . . Sometimes the commander-in-chief found himself yearning after the simple, carefree years he had enjoyed before the weight of fame and responsibility burdened his horizons. He had never forgotten his canny upbringing in the unfashionable tenement in the heart of old Glasgow, with its memories of boyhood evenings tearing along the cobbled Trongate with his young brothers to cheer on the mud-caked Edinburgh coach. Other memories crowded in. The heart-lurching exhilaration of his first command, the satisfaction of seeing off a detachment of American rebels on the tree-fringed coast of Nova Scotia in the knowledge that he had come to terms with fear and was capable of instilling courage by example in his inexperienced men, the youthful thirst for adventure and a widening of horizons.

There was little time to waste on reflection, however. He had headaches innumerable to occupy his mind. Till his guns and cavalry arrived his position at Salamanca was one of acute danger. But General Hope was still a hundred miles south of him and Baird, prevented at the outset by the Corunna junta from disembarking, was now hopelessly behind schedule, battling though he was through rain and mist to bring up his reinforcements fresh from England.

There were domestic matters also. Hester wanted to send him her youngest brother James. There was no real need for another aide but Hester was adept at getting her own way. The lad will be disappointed if it is action he seeks, brooded Moore bitterly. By the time he arrives I shall already be beaten.

Scarcely had the commander-in-chief left table that evening when a travel-stained rider delivered into his hands a despatch of the utmost urgency from Madrid. Motioning the exhausted courier into a comfortable chair Moore broke the seal and scanned the despatch keenly. Kit, in the act of measuring a glass of wine to the courier, glimpsed fleetingly the sag of his general's shoulders beneath the scarlet and gold, the brief despairing closure of the fine eyes.

Calling his military secretary in from the office adjoining, Moore motioned towards the despatch, saying with quiet emphasis, "The worse is come, as I feared. General Castaños's army has been overwhelmed at Tudela."

Colborne snatched up the despatch and read it in silence. Kit remained where he was, heartsick for the general. There was nothing now to stop the French from marching upon Salamanca. The British were the only undefeated force left in northern Spain. In the face of a strength five times their number the incomplete army must now face certain slaughter.

Moore parted the looped window drapes and stared out at the darkened streets beyond. It was almost nine o'clock. Here in the old quarter shadowed by the parish church opposite, the noisy, bustling Salamanca of the Plaza Mayor was eerily banished. Like a city of the dead shrouded in a pall of night, he mused.

A city of the dead . . . His lips compressed. Yet, if I pull out the troops now, he argued, almost surely it will be interpreted by the Spanish Government as a deliberate act of desertion, a running away without a fight. John Hookham Frere, the British envoy in Madrid, was consistently urging for strong action. God only knew how he must react to such a measure.

Although they had never met, the general's relations with Frere were become less than cordial. A bosom friend of Moore's arch-critic, the Foreign Secretary Canning, he had rapidly irritated Sir John by his interference in matters purely military and by the insolence and conceit with which he expressed himself in their correspondence.

Over-caution. It was always over-caution with Frere. And although Sir John Moore had not the least intention of being dictated to by the minister or any other civilian lackey, he could not altogether afford to ignore the fellow's opinion. Frere was spokesman for their country's policy towards Spain and consultation with him must necessarily continue.

Am I justified, brooded Moore, in playing for time? There were, he knew, rumblings of discontent within his general staff, a growing canker of resentment based on the rumour that he was bent on retreating upon Portugal. They were disillusioned and bitterly disappointed, as he was, at the prospect of giving up without ever having fired a shot at the enemy. It must be a humiliating exit, a move highly unpopular with the men. He knew also that some compared him unfavourably with Wellesley and while this was to be expected Moore found it increasingly hard to hide his hurt that they could not or would not understand his reasons for contemplating evacuation.

Resuming his seat he stared at his two majors, then he reached for a quill and drew a sheet of paper towards him.

"The French have a corps at Burgos which will almost certainly now march forward." His mouth compressed into an obstinate line. "I have determined to give the thing up. A junction is now out of the question except by forced marches, and both columns have already encountered heavy snows. No." He shook his head. "Baird must fall back on Corunna and go round to the Tagus to assemble with us there. If the Spaniards still hold out, by taking this army to Cadiz and landing it there we may yet be of use."

He raised his eyes from the wet page, remarking softly, "It is a cruel decision for me to make. I pray they will think the circumstances such as demand it."

Kit privately hoped so too, for the general's sake. For days rumour had persisted throughout the Army that preparations were about to be made to go back to Lisbon. Indignant denials had greeted any suggestion from the local townspeople that such a humiliating report might have foundation. Lord knows, thought Kit, what the reaction will be now. Not even Sir John Moore's immense popularity could lessen the backlash of bitterness which the bombshell must ignite. The Army's sense of betrayal would be absolute.

*　　　*　　　*

Dindie closed her journal and laid it aside. Tonight she had not the heart to write further. The news which Kit had just confided was so incredible, so unbelievable, that she could not take it in. She studied his bare shoulders as he poured water into a bowl and began to lather himself with soap. She no longer felt embarrassment at seeing him undress. Campaign life swiftly banished any notions of false modesty. He was bare to the waist, his body lean and browned by exposure. She drank in the athletic grace of his movements. He looked, she thought admiringly, like a young Apollo.

The French were at Burgos, and coming up fast . . . tightly she closed her eyes, a dread vision washing over her of that same lithe body bloodied to pulp, a sabre dripping wetly with his blood. With a low moan she pressed her lips together. Kit turned, frowning.

"Dindie? . . . Little love, whatever troubles you?" He came and sat beside her on the bed, turning up her face. "What's this?"

His thumb wiped gently at her brimming eyes.

"I — I'm so afraid, Kit." The words jerked out in hiccuped monosyllables. She heard him exclaim, then he took her into his arms pressing his cheek close to her wet face whilst she sobbed out her fears for him in choking gasps.

"Hush, wifeling," he murmured. "Attend to this. The Service trains a man to take care of himself. Be sure I'll not suffer any blasted Frenchman to make a widow of my wife just yet — not when we've been wed only five minutes."

"Are you never afraid, Kit?" she whispered.

"I should be a liar if I said no," he answered softly. "A soldier in battle experiences fear all the time — but he must learn to live with it, Dindie."

She digested his words in silence. In the comfortable security of his arm with her head on his shoulder the dread shadows receded. Tentatively she asked, "Kit, have — have ever you killed anyone?"

"Yes," he replied briefly. "At Egmont, in the Low Countries expedition." He glanced down at her troubled face, stroking her chilblained fingers with his thumb. "Sometimes one must kill or be killed, wifeling. There's nothing vengeful in it."

He hesitated. "Dindie . . . before we left England I had my lawyer draw up a will. No, don't look so — it is right you should know of it. If anything does happen to me you will be well provided for. But nothing shall," he added firmly, alive to the abrupt fear in her glance. "And you ought not to be heeding those scare-mongers in the ranks who boast of having clareted their steel. It's just so much talk, Dindie."

Her eyes, hugely brown in anguish, searched his own for a long moment. He saw her lower lip tremble. Then her arms flung around his neck and she kissed him fiercely, almost defiantly, her breath escaping in a sharp, involuntary sob.

She did not resist as Kit's lips sought hers, gently at first then with a burning deliberation as he felt her response quicken. Her long lashes fluttered open under his kiss and the glow in her velvet eyes raced his heart. But when she experienced the hungry urgency of his caress her body tensed and she pushed him from her in panic and sat up.

"I — I cannot, Kit . . . " Tearfully Dindie smoothed down her rumpled skirts, averting her face so that he might not see her hot shame in having failed him yet again.

"Dindie, wait!" Cursing himself for his clumsiness Kit sprang from the bed. "Lovedy, I'm sorry . . . " He turned her despairingly round to face him. "There is nothing to be afraid of in love, Dindie. Won't you even try to meet me halfway?"

Her lips pressed together mutely and she wrenched free of his restraining grasp and rushed to her own bedchamber, turning the key in the lock.

7

LONG AFTER HE judged her to be asleep Kit lay restless, his thoughts teeming with a confusion to which he could not put a name. Her initial response, so adorably unrestrained and impromptu, had shaken him. Her arms, wound softly around his neck, lips soft and yielding under his mouth betrayed a stirring of womanhood which had both astonished and delighted, firing him with desire for her. She had recognised it, matched his mood, had been on the point of submitting . . . Was it me she ran from, Kit wondered bitterly, or from herself?

They did not meet next morning. Dindie kept to her room, pleading a headache, and Kit sat through breakfast making light of the sly winks and ribald comments at his haggard appearance. He was relieved when the general ordered an intelligence mission to sound out information on the enemy's position. Moore had the uncanny knack of reading a man and Kit had no desire to be quizzed, however kindly, upon his particular problems with Dindie. A few days away from headquarters would be relief, as much to her as to himself, he decided moodily.

November crept to a close amid mutinous grumblings and despair. In the sprawling camps around Salamanca bivouacs were being hastily abandoned and tents taken down. Horses whinnied and mules brayed their unholy discord, and men swore as they transferred sick comrades to screeching bullock-carts for the tortuous haul to the Army hospital at Almeida.

The commander-in-chief witnessed these preparations grim-faced and anxious. His reception as he rode among the men was respectful but subdued. The air hung heavy with resentment. He could read it on every face — the frustration, the censure, the despairing *why?* On each occasion he returned to the Palacio feeling wretched and depressed.

Within hours of his decision to retreat he had called a meeting of his general staff. Stormy protests and in certain quarters near anarchy had greeted his announcement but he refused to be swayed. For a few days longer he intended to hang on at Salamanca. His guns and cavalry might just be able to slip through the tightening French net to join him.

More than once during that second day of December the general read through Frere's latest letter. The fellow seemed incapable of digesting the magnitude of the enemy threat but this particular communication was a sizzler. Any thought of withdrawal must be abandoned. It would, wrote the envoy dramatically, sink the hearts of the whole country.

*   *   *

Dindie dressed for dinner with a heavy heart. Save for the occasional presence of a visiting diplomat with his lady, the commander-in-chief's table was generally devoid of feminine company and she felt wretchedly out of place without Kit. Her disquiet at entering the lofty dining-room alone must have been evident for George Napier at once detached himself from a knot of fellow officers and gallantly tucked her arm through his, announcing that she must meet his eldest brother Charles, whom the chief had invited to dine that evening.

There could be no mistaking the young commander of the 50th Regiment, for his prominent hawk nose and flaring eyebrows were so in the mould of his brother that Dindie's expression of startled disbelief caused both Napiers to burst out laughing.

"You ought to see all eight of us ranged with beaks in profile!" grinned George, effecting introductions. "Charles will tell you how our Irish schoolfellows in Celbridge dubbed our house 'The Eagles' Nest'. By the way, lad, don't elect to favour Dindie with your devastating charm — she inclines to a blue cavalry coat above any of us Mud Crushers.''

Dindie's despondency could not long remain in face of such teasing banter and before dinner was much progressed she felt almost gay once more. How she wished a little of their carefree spirits might convey to the drawn figure at the head of the long table. Even with gruff old Colonel Graham returned from Madrid, Moore's commanding presence lacked its accustomed verve. Dindie's heart went out to him. He looked so alone, crushed almost. Instinctively she turned to George Napier, her eyes troubled.

"He is heartsick at the necessity for retreat," explained Napier, quietly. "They are all against him, save for Anderson and Paget." His burning glance swept contemptuously down the double line of scarlet-clad general officers. "Oh, I know Kit says I'm biased because I've been with the chief five years but it makes me see red to hear 'em all accuse Sir John of running from the French when they know damn well it is a decision he cannot have taken lightly!"

"Steady, George," murmured his brother with a warning glance toward Dindie. "We're not on the battlefield. I should think there is every hope the chief will reconsider, if Graham's report has foundation."

"What report?" asked Dindie quickly. Cold alarm caused the flickering candelabra set at intervals down the polished table to blur in her vision.

"Have you not heard, Dindie? Boney has halted his advance towards us and is moving on Madrid! Why, every Spanish Johnny able to handle a spade is digging trenches like fury round the capital to keep him out — though Lord knows they cannot hope to withstand for long against his artillery."

"You mean — the French will not risk an attack here?"

"More likely Boney believes us to have already abandoned Salamanca, Mrs Fane — or it could be he is simply thumbing his nose at us and has launched an all-out conquest of the south."

Charles Napier knit his black brows thoughtfully. "Curse his blood, are we never to come to grips?"

Dindie offered a silent prayer of thanksgiving for the deliverance. A sudden longing for Kit overwhelmed her, so sharp in its intensity that she was forced to clench her knuckles, and with the thought of him her unhappiness returned.

The candles guttered low that night in Moore's private quarters. Napoleon's electrifying move opened up possibilities which all the general's instincts told him to seize. It confirmed beyond doubt the numerous intelligence reports indicating that the Emperor was ignorant of the British positions. Whatever the reasons Moore held one powerful trump card — surprise. If he moved swiftly enough by striking north-east towards the River Douro he could disrupt Napoleon's life-line, the vital food supplies upon which the French Army depended. The Emperor would be forced to return north to deal with him, thus enabling the Spaniards to organise an effective defence of their capital.

It was a dangerous game and Moore knew it. If the plan worked the British Army would become the fox to Napoleon's hounds and be forced to run for its life over the mountains. Dare he risk his country's sole military strength in order to give the Spaniards yet another chance to prove themselves? The dilemma gave little hope of sleep that night.

Two days later Sir John Hope with his precious guns and cavalry reached Alba de Tormes, only fifteen miles from Salamanca. The men were dog-tired, with faces drawn from sleeplessness and knifing cold. Moore, who had ridden out early to greet his third-in-command, felt a lump form in his throat at the spirit and cheerfulness which their gruelling hardships could not quench.

He was not long returned to his desk when a footstep in the outer office disturbed him. Moore frowned. His aides were all out on duty and Colborne had also been called briefly away. Throwing wide the door he was astonished to find young Mrs Fane, who drew back in confusion at his entrance.

"I beg your pardon," stammered Dindie, reddening under the

commander-in-chief's air of surprise. "I hoped to find Kit returned . . . " Her voice trailed off into embarrassed silence.

"Major Fane arrived back just under an hour ago. I sent him to have breakfast." Moore's eyebrows lifted quizzically. "I should have judged he would want to be reunited with you first — or am I casting about like a Paul Pry?"

For a second she seemed about to cry, then with forced brightness replied, "What can you mean, sir?"

"Only that you have the look of my sister Jeannie when she is about to unleash the water-spouts." He regarded her warmly. "I am never too busy to talk to a lady, Mrs Fane. Will you not keep me company until your husband returns?" He motioned her to a comfortable chair but she remained uncertainly by the door, clasping and unclasping the strings of her reticule.

"Mrs Fane," declared Moore, smiling faintly. "Politeness forbids me to sit until you do — and being so much the taller I find it disconcerting to address myself to your bonnet-strings."

Dindie laughed at this gentle chiding and accepted a chair. The general drew up another, by no means sorry for the interruption.

"Now," when they were comfortable, "have you quarrelled?"

Dindie shook her head quickly. "I had liefer not discuss it, if you please. The fault is altogether of my making." She glanced up shyly. "Have you many sisters, sir?"

"Only the one, but I have four brothers." He allowed himself the pleasure of drawing her out. So like Caroline, he told himself, and yet with an indefinable charm all her own. "Kit tells me your father was a doctor. So was mine, although he much preferred wielding the novelist's pen to a knife."

Dindie warmed to his approachability, sensing genuine interest in the generous, penetrating eyes. He asked questions about her home in Dean and in turn spoke with affection of his own mother, now in her seventies, who resided with his sister at Brook Farm in Cobham, home of his sailor brother Graham, whom he referred to with teasing drollery as the Commodore.

"As you may perceive, I am really only the lodger there." The

100

strong mouth hovered on a smile. "Tell me, how do you respond to being a soldier's wife?"

Dindie considered hard before making reply. "If you mean do I enjoy being with the Army, sir, then I do — more than anything." A sadness crept into her voice and she continued quietly, "But if you ask how I shape as a wife to Major Fane you must apply to him, for I am not c-competent to — "

Fiercely, she searched for a handkerchief and blew her nose. "What are the qualities necessary to make a good Army wife, General? Pray do not smile. It — it is important to me."

Moore regarded her searchingly, sure now that he had put his finger on the root of her unhappiness. Army wives as a rule faced the worst possible introduction to matrimony. Their lot demanded more than the average talents necessary to keeping a marriage together. Fane was a first-class aide but he was something of a flirt. This inexperienced young bride was evidently suffering heartache as a result of the transition.

Smiling earnestly down into the woe-begone little face opposite he replied reassuringly, "Resolve here and now to become your husband's strength, Mrs Fane. Work at it, forget self-pity, be a devoted and cheerful helpmeet to him. Remember, my officers have worries enough on campaign without wives indulging in the vapours." He rose briskly. "Now, if you will wait downstairs, I shall send your major to you presently."

*   *   *

"Are you saying General Moore has ordered you to — to take leave for the remainder of the day, Kit?" Dindie's eyes widened in disbelief.

"Provided I spend it with you. He was particular on that score." Kit regarded her hesitantly. "Dindie, you haven't told him anything about our — about the other night?"

"Do you judge me to be so indiscreet?" she whispered hotly, turning away.

"Don't let us quarrel — not when we have the whole day ahead of us." Kit reached for her hand, pleading in his voice. "I've missed you, Dindie," he added, very quietly.

She looked uncertainly into his face, colouring rosily.

"H-ave you?" It was a foolish remark, totally inadequate for their situation. The warmth of his hand was like a fire and her heart pounded so loudly against her ribs that she felt he must hear. She wanted to cry out that every aching hour of their separation had been to her like a lifetime, every remembrance of his touch a searing bitter-sweetness — but all she could say in her confusion was, "Kit — I promised to go riding with Jamie this afternoon. It — it slipped my mind."

She saw her husband's mouth tighten in the manner she now knew so well. "I suppose Jamie has shown you round the cathedral already — and the House of the Shells, and the pleasure-gardens and river-walk! Any visit there in my company can only be an anti-climax. It strikes me you might have done better to marry Drummond in the first place!"

"That is unfair! I had rather have gone with you, Kit. Only you never asked me."

"Well, I'm asking you now. Go fetch your shawl."

"But what about Jamie? I — I gave my word, Kit."

"Jamie," returned the major, with something like relish in his voice, "may go to the devil!"

To argue was useless. They walked into town in silence, save for stilted exchanges. But by the time the Plaza Mayor was reached Kit's anger had cooled in the December sunshine and Dindie was eager to match his softened mood. She found his eyes resting several times upon her when he thought her unaware, and knew he was trying to find words to broach the subject which hung between them like an oppressive weight.

"Who was that smarmy Frenchman I passed on the stairs arguing with Colborne? He had the look of a brigand out of theatrical farce."

Dindie laughed, relieved to find his thoughts on a different tack. "His name is Colonel de Charmilly, and he is an émigré, I believe,

102

from England. Do you not remember, Kit — he called at headquarters once before with a despatch which he had found? Napier says he was once a coal-merchant! I think he looks more of an adventurer."

"What the deuce is he about at headquarters?"

Dindie wrinkled her brows. "I overheard him tell Major Colborne that he was the bearer of a letter from Mr Frere in Madrid."

"Good God!" Kit burst out laughing in amazement. The oily Frenchman was exactly Frere's style. He could guess how Moore would view any dealings with this questionable fish.

"Oh, Kit — look! Did ever you see anything so delightful?"

A procession of diminutive figures in bridal white had entered the square, little girls in first communion dress each carrying a prayer book. The solemn child faces were partially hid by flowing white veils of lace each surmounted by a chaplet of flowers.

It was an unexpectedly lovely sight. Faces aglow with self-conscious piety, the youthful procession circled the Plaza Mayor, extending in length and density until it seemed to Dindie there must be hundreds of tiny bride figures forming this massive ring. Preceding them was a statue of the Madonna in silver crown and blue robe and the whole, set against the background of tall arcaded houses, was so imbued with the indefinable Spanish sense of style that Dindie drew an exclamation of sheer admiration.

Instead of following the procession into the cathedral's candlelit interior they sat in the warm sunlight of a secluded garden near by where a minute fountain gurgled happily. Dindie felt a deep contentment steal over her. Kit's arm relaxed about her shoulder and she guessed he must welcome this release of tension as much as herself. As if reading her thoughts he dipped a finger in the fountain pool and traced the line of her snub nose.

"Why did you run from me the other night, Dindie?" he asked softly. "Am I such a Bluebeard that you cannot bear me to touch you?"

"No," she whispered chokily.

Kit glanced down at her, continuing with deceptive casualness.

"Your step-father must have hurt you badly. There was more to it, I think, than his simply attempting to kiss you."

Dindie cast him a swift, fearful look and tried to shy away, but his arm secured her with a gentle pressure. He waited, resting his chin against her brow. At length Dindie stirred and in a thin faraway voice stammered, "He — he tried to violate me."

She drew a long shuddering sigh and buried her face in his chest. Kit held her fast, the murder in his heart coupled with an overwhelming sense of relief that he had finally coaxed her into admitting what he had come to suspect as the root of her fears.

"Why did you not confide this before, wifeling? Not all men are like Harker, you know."

"But it is important to a man — to have a wife who is willing to play the ace to his jack?" she faltered, raising her head.

Making a mental note to ensure a stricter curb on her opportunities of overhearing and adopting the gutter terms used by the men, however innocently framed, Kit replied gently, "A satisfying relationship rarely happens overnight. It must be nurtured by respect and trust — and affection. We have had so little time together . . . you might have married a stranger, for all we know about each other. I'm willing to wait, Dindie," he added softly.

"Kit . . . if you really want me to — "

"No," he smiled, smoothing the hair from her brow. "You must come to me of your own will. Now — shall we look round the cathedral?"

Feeling happier than she had for a long time Dindie accompanied him into the cool interior. She marvelled at the elaborate painted retable to the High Altar and stood some minutes in earnest contemplation of the brooding effigies of the Virgin and Apostles. The tiny bride-figures had left but the candles they had lit remained flickering brightly against the gloom. An excitable little priest in tasselled robes approached, explaining that for fear of the French the valuables of the cathedral had regrettably been hidden away. None the less one or two pieces of gold plate were still on view and an exquisite jewelled crucifix over which Dindie exclaimed.

"I think I never saw anything so magnificent," she breathed. "See, Kit — how the stones wink back at one."

"Emeralds." Kit examined the altar-piece with interest. "I should judge it to be worth a cool five hundred."

"You are funning, surely! Why, it is no size at all."

As they came into the winter sun once more Dindie remarked, "Is that not Private Flannigan coming up the street?"

Kit followed her pointing hand, then she saw his colour change. As the dragoon strutted into view Dindie perceived he was not alone. On his arm was the gypsy girl Paquita. On seeing Kit the Irishman sprang off an exaggerated salute which just stopped short of insolence.

" 'Tis a grand day, Major." He leered at his sultry companion and added, " 'Specially when the company suits like a second skin."

Paquita's mouth curved in appreciation but her glance was all for Kit. Briefly she looked Dindie up and down with a mocking contempt that chilled Dindie's spine, though she did not know why. It was not simply that this girl had the power to set a man on fire for her simply by looking at him. She was eyeing Kit with the intimate confidence of possession, as though an unspoken bond drew them together by some Gordian knot of which Dindie was ignorant. Kit's mouth hardened in anger. Then he strode on, leaving Dindie standing hurt and bewildered, knowing he had forgotten her presence.

Fear rose in her throat as she ran after him. Yes, she thought bitterly, you say you will wait for me, Kit. Yet you burn for her — and will dally with her if you can.

Corporal Jackson had also wound up at the cathedral. It had not been his original intention. He had been browsing round the shops staring longingly at the exorbitantly priced goods on offer, wishing there was some small thing he might buy to take home to his Mary. Fine hopes of that, he mused gloomily, when he could ill afford even the few pesetas which he had been obliged to lay out in necessaries. Pay was already five weeks in arrears and God only knew where he was to find the money for doctor's bills if Mary got worse. It worried him sick so that he could barely sleep most nights.

Somehow or other in his preoccupation he took a wrong turning and found himself at the ancient town walls, staring into a ditch where a tribe of miserable beggars were lying quite naked in the thin sunshine employed in freeing each other from vermin.

Poverty was no stranger to Jackson but these wretches could excite no sympathy within him, so enmeshed was he in his own troubles. At the end of a gloomy alley the cathedral loomed, imposing, beckoning. He went in.

*   *   *

"Colonel de Charmilly is still waiting to see you, sir."

Moore groaned. The greasy Charmilly was the last man on earth he desired to see that night. As for Frere, if he had the impertinence to send communications through so doubtful a channel as this vain, ingratiating customer . . .

"Bring me the letter, Napier — but leave that fellow outside!"

"Sir, he refuses to hand it over save into your hands." Napier wished the general might not talk so loudly. Charmilly was only a step away on the other side of the wall.

"Then make him wait until I have leisure to see him."

Moore returned his attention to the letter he had been reading and Napier nipped smartly from the room, thinking to himself that the chief was in a fine dander tonight. He hoped the toadying Charmilly would be discouraged from his purpose but no, the colonel was only too honoured to wait.

Moore studied the Madrid despatch before him. It was from the new Junta of Defence, begging him to aid the city's defences with British troops. Over and over he dissected the odds. Graham had told how the spirit of resistance burned high in the capital, yet Moore had too often experienced the evaporation of similar

106

enthusiasms to be easily swayed. But if he stuck to his decision to retreat and Madrid fell, what then?

It was then he remembered his unwelcome visitor. As well have the business over and be shot of him. It soon became clear, however, that the fellow had been sent by Frere expressly to persuade Moore to alter his decision. The fate of Spain, warned the envoy in his letter which Charmilly handed over, was dependent absolutely upon the decision which Moore chose to adopt. It was an awesome responsibility. One way or the other he must decide, and quickly.

Throughout that night as the minutes ticked relentlessly on, light shone beneath the general's door. His aides waited anxiously for a summons. At last an abrupt command preceded the handing out of a despatch to be taken immediately to Sir David Baird's headquarters. Moore's course was decided.

The following morning the familiar figure of Charmilly arrived once more with a request to speak with General Moore, only to be firmly refused by Captain Harry Percy, alone of all the aides not out on duty. The general was finishing despatches.

"*Mon Dieu* — but it is vital I see the general! There is a letter for his eyes alone! It is necessary he should read it *tout de suite!*"

Not for all the universe was Harry Percy prepared to stick his head round Moore's door. He went to find Colborne.

"What does this mean, Colonel de Charmilly?" Moore's furious figure stood in the doorway. "*A letter from Mr Frere?* And why did you not give it me last night?"

Trembling visibly the podgy colonel followed him into the familiar writing-room and answered that Mr Frere had instructed he should not hand it over unless it proved necessary.

"*Necessary?*" Moore's eyes blazed. Snatching the letter he thundered out a denunciation of the Frenchman's deception.

"General — " Charmilly's voice was a squeak. The commander-in-chief was looking murderous and the only door was closed.

"Sir, will you be so good as to go near the fire and let me read that letter?" Moore strode to the window, broke the seal on the communication and read through the contents with mounting fury and astonishment. Frere was threatening him — there was no other word — in the most impudent terms that unless he withdrew his decision to retreat the matter would be referred before a meeting of his fellow generals! It was not merely insulting. This was blackmail of the highest order.

*　　*　　*

Kit galloped his horse through the rounded archway of the Palacio and flung himself from the saddle, heated but exhilarated. Like the other aides he prided himself in being able to ride twelve miles in an hour. On this occasion he had beaten his own record from Hope's headquarters by fully fifteen minutes.

He took the stairs three at a time, whistling cheerfully only to veer sharply aside in astonishment as a terror-stricken Colonel de Charmilly scuttled from Moore's office and passed him on the landing, almost falling head-first in his haste.

"Out, sir! And stay out!" Moore's furious roar echoed like thunder through the old walls of the Palacio. Never had Kit seen his commander-in-chief in such a taking. Colborne and Harry Percy were standing open-mouthed in awe. Then unexpectedly Sir John gave vent to a mocking laugh as the impertinence of it all struck his fancy and he strode back to his office with a beckoning nod for them to follow.

Within the spacious writing-room the general broke his decision. Baird's force must turn about and converge with them on the city of Burgos, which lay directly on Napoleon's vital life-line. Retreat was abandoned.

"What is passing at Madrid may be decisive to the fate of Spain," he declared with conviction. "We must be on hand to aid and to take advantage of whatever happens."

At their jubilant shouts his tired smile broadened in quiet satisfaction. He was certain now of having made the right decision, as he had never been over withdrawal. At best the brilliant stroke might succeed. At worst . . .

"If all else fails," he continued soberly, "at least it will be apparent that we stuck to the Spaniards long after they themselves had given up their cause as lost."

"Sir, it's the most stupendous news! We shall lick 'em to fits." Napier's eyes blazed with purpose. He punched Kit playfully on the shoulder. "You are uncommonly silent, Major. Don't tell us you had as lief see the fleas of Lisbon again."

"I was thinking of my wife's reaction," returned Kit quietly. "She is only sixteen —and very much afraid for me."

"You are right to be concerned, Fane." Moore became all at once grave. "For if the bubble bursts and Madrid falls, we shall have a run for it."

*   *   *

Dindie was dressing for dinner when Kit burst in and seized her about the waist, announcing breathlessly that the withdrawal had been countermanded. Immediately the old fears clutched at her insides. Retreat had spelled a degree of safety. Now . . .

Disengaging his hands she sat down before the dressing-table and began pulling a brush through her waist-length hair with terse strokes. She was wearing a round gown of pomona green which flattered her golden brown skin. The looking-glass told her that she looked attractive, and although she had blushed at the revealing lines which accentuated the warm hollow between her breasts she had overcome her inhibitions, determined to earn Kit's admiration. Now all paled into insignificance.

He came and stood behind her, lightly caressing her bare shoulder. "You have lovesome hair, Dindie."

She half-inclined her head and rested one cheek against his fingers. "How soon do we leave Salamanca?" she whispered.

"The leading regiments will march out within the next few days. Speed is essential now."

Kit watched her part her light brown hair, intrigued by the dexterity with which she swept it into a Clytie knot on top, allowing wispy tendrils to cluster appealingly over her ears and forehead.

The lingering fragrance of attar of roses filled the bedchamber as she replaced the stopper in the scent bottle. Reflected in the glass her face was strained yet composed, as if she were determined to smother her agony of suffering.

They were interrupted by Napier's voice on the stair. Next instant Jamie burst in, his face flushed from hard riding.

"Kit, there has been a theft . . . some crucifix went missing from the cathedral yesterday." He sat down heavily. "It turned up in C Troop."

Flannigan, thought Kit, after his initial shock. It had to be Flannigan. Deuce take his miserable Irish blood, didn't he have the wit to realise that looting was a capital offence? The creature had pulled out all the stops this time.

"Strangely enough, it's not Flannigan."

Kit was unaware of having voiced his suspicions aloud. Jamie's quiet rejoinder brought his head up abruptly.

"The crucifix was found in Corporal Jackson's effects."

"But that's impossible! Jackson is steady as they come! There must be some mistake."

In the glow from the oil lamp Jamie's face was etched with weariness. "That's what I tried to tell Colonel Stewart, but he refuses to heed, says he means to make Jackson an example to deter any others."

"Kit, you must speak for Tom!" Dindie slipped to her husband's side and caught urgently at his hands. "He is a good man — why, you have often said he has earned his stripes a dozen times over." She hesitated. "You — do believe him to be innocent?"

Kit passed a hand across his brow. Who knew to what lengths despair and a sick wife might drive a soldier?

"Where is Jackson now? With the provost marshal?"

Jamie shook his head. "There is to be a drumhead court-martial at eight hundred hours tomorrow." He stared hard at Kit, desperate appeal in his glance. "I ask no favour for myself — but Jackson is no thief! Will you try to convince Stewart?"

"Will it do any good if I do? If Jackson is for the Bloody Assize he can expect no leniency. You know that." Kit sighed deeply. "I've never been precisely popular with Stewart."

He looked directly into his wife's entreating brown eyes. Her faith in him was so bloody implicit. Involuntarily, he rubbed his thumb against her cheek. "Well, of course I mean to try, lovedy —but Heaven help Tom Jackson if I fail," he added softly.

8

EIGHTY-SIX. EIGHTY-SEVEN. Round swung the lash, falling with a sickening thud on the quivering flesh. Tom Jackson slumped in agony, searing pain racking his bloodied back. There was blood everywhere —running into his boots, down his bare shoulders, from his mouth where he had bit through his lip to staunch the screams, blood saturating his blue-grey campaign overalls . . .

"Eighty-eight," roared the farrier-major in a clear voice. Again. the steady tap of the drum, the drawn-out agony of anticipation, the waiting for the lash to scream through his flesh. He closed his eyes screwing his courage to emerge from this hell with dignity, if he emerged at all. The cold steel of the triangle to which he was secured penetrated his semi-consciousness, pulling him from the abyss back to the reality of pain.

Through a red mist he made out the taut faces of his comrades ranged four or five deep on all sides, the entire regiment assembled to witness his humiliation. The chaplain was there with the adjutant and Colonel Stewart. Faces, a sea of faces pitying, mocking, horror-stricken. He saw one dragoon turn away vomiting.

"Ninety-one." The farrier-sergeants changed over every twenty-five lashes, didn't they? Blackness was caving in and still the relentless agony continued unabated. He was thankful they had chosen a spot outside the town. Blood ran down his throat, choking him . . . Dear Lord, he could hear his own low moaning . . . too weak even to scream.

Ninety-six. Ninety-seven. Two hundred lashes was the sentence, wasn't it? The singing in his ears was growing louder. He could not think straight any more but he knew he would never last out.

They were changing over now. The surgeon was come up to feel his pulse. Jackson prayed that his hell might be terminated whilst at the same time willing it to continue, that they might all see he could take his touching over like a man.

The surgeon nodded for the punishment to proceed and the strokes continued with savage regularity to the drum's tap and the impassive count of the farrier-major.

In the frozen ranks drawn up to witness the sickening spectacle Daniel Flannigan watched Jackson's ghastly contortions with a satisfaction born of hate. Promised I'd fix it proper for you, Corporal, he gloated, twisting his mouth into a smile. As neat a job as ever he'd set his hand to. Pity about the spoil —but Dan Flannigan was not one of your amateurs fool enough to try disposing of Church property. It was enough to have Jackson taking the rap, see his writhing back ploughed to jelly, his precious stripes taken away, his degradation absolute.

Dindie gripped her pony's bridle. Her stomach heaved, she felt sick, she had been determined not to look —now horror held her fascinated. In front of her pony a huddle of wives stood rooted, shock depriving them of their accustomed ebullience. No matter how often enacted the ritual lost nothing of its macabre chill.

At the one hundred-and-eighteenth lash the bloodsoaked mass of flesh on the triangle gave a convulsive jerk and then hung limp. The surgeon raised his hands, the counting ceased and an audible sigh of relief went up from officers and men alike. The colonel ordered Jackson's insensible form to be untriced immediately and the waiting hospital orderlies ran forward to carry him off.

Dindie found herself trembling. Suddenly all was again bustle, the musicians striking up a jarring march-tune, bugles shrilling their imperative message, the serried square of dark blue dispersed with cool precision. Only a livid stain on the frost-white grass remained to record the grizzly event.

"Are you all right, Dindie?" Stony-faced, Kit pushed a path

through the mounting cavalrymen to her side. She nodded, devoid of emotion.

"What will happen to him?" she whispered.

"He is to be taken to the Army hospital at Almeida. As soon as they pronounce him fit he will rejoin the regiment." He gripped her hands tightly. "I'm sorry you had to witness this — this . . . " He forced down an oath, too choked with disgust to continue. "Keep with the Baggage column," he commanded, and strode quickly away.

Tom Jackson lay face down on a hastily-spread blanket. Someone had forced a tot of rum between his lips but nothing could dull the pain, the raw screwing pain. Every touch brought him out in a sweat and the frosty air so knifed through his open wounds that he was forced to cry out. His eyes, sunk and fixed, stared about him impervious to the surgeon's methodical sponging and bandaging. The blood which had congealed in rivulets gave his skin a glazed and coppered effect horrible to behold.

It was as much as Kit could manage not to vomit there and then. Bending down, he said quietly, "Jackson?"

The dull eyes flickered in recognition. To his horror Kit saw the corporal's drooping face turn wet with tears.

"I didn't do it, Major. Honest," he whispered.

Kit wiped away the sticky blood from the grey lips, barely trusting himself to speak so enraged was he at the broken, tortured spectacle before him.

"I know that," he answered grimly, "and I mean to find who did."

He remained with Jackson talking, comforting until the bullock-cart's excruciating scrape was heard trundling up. God help you, thought Kit fervently, as he supervised Jackson's transfer to the unyielding receptacle. The jolting on that infernal mountain road must inevitably tear off plasters and re-open the sickening lacerations. In this primitive conveyance where the wheels were solid wood and so badly constructed that they were not even round, every jerk would be screeching, agonised hell.

Two days later Moore himself left Salamanca with his staff following the infantry column which had already taken the road to Alaejos, protected by a cavalry screen. His two main bodies of horse were advancing by another route to join up with Baird's cavalry from Corunna. If luck held the entire strength of the British Army should be concentrated at Burgos within the week.

The roads were slippery with frost and the sky clear and still blue. The men were in good spirits, which was just as well, reflected Kit, for the pace was furious. But they were going after the French at last, and if the rate of march increased daily, and the stages grew longer, and at each halt they were asleep before their aching bodies reached the frozen ground, they were sustained by the prospect of a fight.

"Sure, we'll beat 'em," Kit overheard one Irish infantryman exclaim. "By Saint Patrick, we'd beat 'em so easy the general means to march us to death, and fight them after!"

Pray Heaven you are proved right, murmured Kit, unscrewing his canteen and drinking thirstily. The chief was driving the pace hard. He thought fleetingly of his own regiment which had just notched up the opening shots of the campaign by surprising a detachment of enemy cavalry at the village of Rueda. He wished he might have been present. It was surprising how he missed the familiar grind of regimental life. There was something worthwhile in transforming a set of raw, civilian rag-tags into professional dragoons, witnessing that unique love-hate relationship which the mounted soldier develops with the dumb, wilful animal which must be mucked out, fed and groomed at the ungodly hour of five every morning.

There were other aspects less savoury. The bullish regimentation breaking spirit and individuality. Kit had constantly to remind himself that the British Army was drawn for the most part from thieves, cut-throats and rogues, dependent absolutely on the Service. It fed the ranker, clothed him, gave him a shilling a day and took back sixpence for his rations and another fourpence so that his washing might be done by the wives on the strength. Little wonder, thought Kit wryly, that so many blew their remaining twopence on Hollands gin.

Fortunately, there was always good leavening such as young Flower and Jackson. Kit stared moodily beyond the halted column to the bleak plateau across which they had come, a countryside eerily devoid of birds and habitation save for the odd mud-walled shack of a peasant. He had tried, God knows, to save Jackson but Charles Stewart had chosen to pull rank on him, settling the score, thought Kit disgustedly, over the question of Dindie at the expense of an innocent man. Until now he had respected his colonel. Even though Stewart was held to be vain, making much of the fact that he was Lord Castlereagh's half-brother and with a liking for intrigue, he was a first-class soldier.

How unjust, how bloody unjust the system was! Impatiently, Kit pushed his frustration aside and turned his thoughts to Dindie. Despite her pleas he had compelled her to ride with the other women at the rear for safety's sake. His eyes softened. She was grown part of him. He found himself missing the relaxing warmth of those moments at the end of the day when they would lie talking quietly in bed discussing the day's events, or laughing together over some absurdity or other. It was during one of these satisfying interludes lying in the crook of his arm that she had confessed the intimate details of her experience at Harker's hands. It was clear that only by the grace of God and the unexpected return of Miss Harker had the ultimate horror been averted. Kit's mouth tensed. Afterwards, she had fallen asleep in his arms like a child.

Later that day he found his mind returning to another matter. How long, he wondered, had that bitch Paquita been giving her favours to the Irishman? If it were anyone but Flannigan, he thought savagely, it would mean nothing . . . She had the morals of a cat and it was laughable to suppose she would keep herself aloof when half the Army wanted her. But the realisation of having shared her body with that pox-ridden weasel induced within Kit a revulsion both against her and himself. Seeing her outside the cathedral at Salamanca standing next to his innocent young wife he had known bitter shame. Oh, Paquita knew how to excite, was capable of tantalising him to ungovernable heights of passion that left them both satisfyingly exhausted.

But it was the lonely hurt in Dindie's eyes, the shocked realisation of seeing him lust after a strumpet, which had filled him with so bitter a sense of degradation that he had walked on, unable to meet her clear gaze. She had not mentioned the incident after and he knew his wife well enough to understand that her hurt was too deep for words.

*　　　*　　　*

The following day a sheaf of captured enemy despatches were brought in to Moore's headquarters at Alaejos. It was clear from their contents that Napoleon's strength was far greater than anyone had supposed — well over 300,000 men. But the plum had been a letter from the Emperor's chief-of-staff to Marshal Soult, giving precise details of French positions and expected march routes. It was evident that the enemy had no inkling of the closeness of the British presence. Soult was cordially regaled with affairs in Madrid, which had capitulated even as Moore wrestled over the odds. The shops and theatres were once again open, ran the letter, and Napoleon was enjoying the best of health.

For Moore it was an opportunity without parallel. Soult was only a hundred miles away due north commanding a modest force. Within hours Henry Hardinge was galloping furiously with orders to halt the advance to Burgos. All divisions were now to converge at Mayorga, by forced marches if necessary. Marshal Soult, Duke of Dalmatia, was about to experience a direct and unsuspecting slash to his rear.

On December 15th the pace was doubled. The Army crossed the Douro river in two columns under snow-laden skies and a shrieking wind. Dindie crouched low in the saddle, burrowing her face against the sodden mane of her pony as a blinding storm enveloped the baggage-train. The white fury pitted into her riding-habit and down her neck. It was impossible to see more than a yard ahead.

117

Behind her riflemen of the rearguard swore richly as several of their number fell. Dindie felt a comforting sense of safety in their presence. Kit had explained that the Light Bobs of the 95th were trained as skirmishers. They were equipped with the specialised Baker rifle and their distinctive dark green uniforms were a necessary camouflage, enabling them to blend almost unseen with rocks and scrub.

As suddenly as it had come, the snowstorm ceased and the waggons rumbled forward once more with their cargo of women and young children huddled behind the tarpaulin hoops or clinging to the roofing, and all pinched with cold and hunger, for the killing pace left no time to spare for cooking.

But they were now in enemy-held country and gruelling night marches were inevitable. The strain on nerves became intolerable as vigilance and a compulsory silence were added to biting cold and fatigue. At one point blue lights were seen to rise at some distance which might or might not have been signals to the French of their approach; bodies tensed, but the column reached Toro unmolested to a tumultuous reception from the townspeople.

Cannon roared from the ramparts and the streets were lined with crowds shouting *"Viva! Viva los Ingleses!"* As the green-jacketed riflemen of the 95th Regiment swung into the main square in their inimitable rapid march behind a band of thirty bugle horns, figs and grapes were pressed into their hands, and some bold jades ran from the crowd to plant kisses on hands and cheeks, to the evident delight of the wise-cracking Light Bobs. Ladies fluttered handkerchiefs from every balcony and Dindie waved delightedly back. This carnival-like welcome was so unexpected, so different from the accustomed Spanish apathy and distrust which had so far accompanied the advance, when whole villages barred doors and windows to prevent the houses being used as billets. Best of all was the knowledge that Kit was waiting for her at the general's headquarters.

She ran into his waiting arms wordless with happiness. Every thorn of doubt and grief when she recalled that gypsy trull was banished in his crushing embrace which took away her breath, leaving her ribs bruised with a sweet ache. Then he bent and kissed her tenderly on the mouth.

"Welcome back, little wife," he whispered.

They left Toro the next morning, splodging through streets foot deep in mud and rooting pigs, with Dindie riding close beside her husband. On the evening of December 19th, Baird's troops entered Mayorga, dragging their feet through the heavy snow-drifts, and the Army was united at last.

They rested at Mayorga all next day. Dindie remained huddled in her blanket after Kit had departed for headquarters. Her limbs ached dreadfully. She had tried rubbing in oil of wintergreen but the cramping pains refused to go away. By noon she felt able to dress and seek out Kit.

She tried the *posada* in the square and found it packed with officers intent upon dice but Kit was not among them. Napier had directed her to the quartermaster-general's office but Kit had already left there. A *muletero* wearing a cuirass of strong buff leather passed her with his droves of mules, each laden down with pigskins of wine. Shambling behind she recognised the Irishman Flannigan from Kit's old troop. The pelisse buttoned over his dolman jacket was bulging in front with some concealed object, obviously live. Seeing Dindie he stopped dead, eyeing her with furtive unease.

"Have you seen Major Fane?" she asked breathlessly. Her head was aching now. How she wished she had remained in the warmth of their attic billet.

"Well now." Flannigan studied her with an insolent grin. He knew damn well where Fane was, and sure the Lord was affording Dan Flannigan the broth of a chance to get back at him for his bloody fatigues in the past. Days on end emptying stinking latrine-buckets . . . His shifty face looked Dindie over. First Jackson, now Fane. It was too good to miss.

"Is it the Major you'd be afther now? Well, you've come to the

119

right one in Dan Flannigan for I seed him not five minutes since outside the stables."

And with Irish luck yez'll just be in grand time, he thought maliciously, watching her step gingerly over the slippery cobbles to the convent.

The troop-horses had been put up in the convent cloisters. They watched with patient eyes as Dindie searched through their rough stalls calling Kit's name. The crumbling stonework held a chilling air of desolation. Pain seared her head, forcing her to rest. When she felt well enough to open her eyes it was to find herself looking directly through the arches to the main convent building. It was then she noticed her husband and Paquita.

Oblivious to her presence they stood in the shadows intent on a long, protracted kiss. Dindie gasped aloud, frozen to immobility by the discovery. It was a lie, a trick of the light, anything! A choking sob rose in her throat. So it was true. All the fears she had harboured, the niggling doubts, all crystallised before her eyes.

Barely able to see what she did Dindie crept away, terrified lest Kit should look up and discover her. That girl! If he wanted to philander surely he might choose someone worthy of him? A slut . . . a common slut. Laying her head down on the silken mane of a chestnut Dindie closed her eyes, broken-hearted.

Had she glanced up then she would have seen the twisted grin of Dan Flannigan rejoicing over her grief from just outside the convent railing.

Back in the spartan attic billet Dindie flung herself on to the neatly folded blanket, heaving sobs tearing her apart. Nausea all at once swept over her and she struggled to reach the washbowl, violently sick. The pain in her head was blinding and she felt faint.

It was thus that Jamie found her, kneeling before the overturned basin exhausted with weeping. In her hysteria she mistook him for Kit and railed wildly at him before collapsing spent in his arms.

"Dindie . . . " Horrified, Jamie caught her, staring with alarm into her raw-red eyes. All at once the gist of her violent outburst became meaningful.

"My dear." Awkwardly his hand reached out to touch her hair. "I'm right sorry."

That single spontaneous gesture destroyed Dindie's remaining efforts at restraint. Brokenly she clung to him, burying her head against his coat, her shoulders heaving piteously. James Drummond fought to keep an iron rein on his emotions. Standing there supporting her, feeling her hot tears splash his hand, he knew as he had never before dared to recognise that his feelings toward this young child-wife ran more deep than they had any right to.

Horror and despair overwhelmed him. One heard of men falling for their best friend's wife, but such things happened to other people . . . It was an impossible situation. Jamie closed his eyes tightly then opened them again and glanced down at the brown head pressed into his shoulder. She leaned against him, quiet now, as though she had no more tears left. His mouth tightened. However wrong their situation nothing in the world would induce him to disengage those small hands plucking hopelessly at the silver frogging on his breast.

At length he asked quietly, "How did you find out?"

He listened grimly as she recounted her discovery. When she had done Jamie remained silent for a long moment. Then he drew her chin up gravely. "Have you not tried talking this thing out with Kit?" he queried.

"How can I, Jamie?" Dindie swallowed painfully. "Do you imagine I can hope to compete with her? — I know what was agreed — what our relationship was to be but . . . I have only ever wanted to be Kit's wife and to have his babies. And he said he would wait . . . he — he promised . . . Is it so wrong to want him?"

The edge in her voice rose, causing him to answer, "Wheesht, lass. Of course it's not wrong. You are his wife."

"No." Her reply was barely above a whisper. "I only married him. That is something quite different." A defeated look stared from her eyes then she laid her head quietly into his coat, saying chokingly, "Jamie, please — please will you hold me? I m-must have someone . . . "

Wordless, James Drummond took the tragic little face in his hands and kissed her gently. He understood perfectly her need. There was nothing of desire in their exchange but her arms flung about his neck and he heard her deep, perceptible sigh as their lips met.

"Now there is a pretty picture, I must say!"

They had neither of them heard Kit enter. He advanced into the cramped room, a peculiar expression charging his countenance. It was fury — and something more which Dindie could not interpret. She froze, heart racing, as Jamie released her. Kit's hair was blown as if he had ridden hard and his eyes — never had she seen them so cold.

"So this is what happens behind my back," he breathed.

"Kit . . . it — it's not what you think!" implored Dindie, suddenly afraid of the fixed purpose in his glance.

He gripped her arm, almost throwing her aside. Before she knew what he intended his fist crashed into Jamie's jaw. Caught unprepared, Jamie staggered backwards with an exclamation.

"Are you man enough to come outside and settle this properly, Drummond?" ground Kit, eyes ablaze.

"Kit, for God's sake — you have it all wrong!" Jamie put a hand to his mouth, wiping away blood.

Kit delivered a crashing oath and made to lunge once more. A little figure flung herself between them, unflinching as the blow intended for Jamie just missed delivering its full force.

"If you have anything to say, Kit, you had best address it to me!" she said, tightly.

"You little idiot — I might have killed you there! Don't you know better than to attempt such a damned stupid move?"

Shaken, Kit pushed the hair from his brow. "Very well, Drummond," he breathed." You can get out of here but don't imagine I'm done with you yet."

"Do you not think it best to hear Dindie's version first?"

122

retorted Jamie angrily. "Are you so confounded blameless that you'd denounce the lass out of hand? What manner of husband are you, for Heaven's sake?"

A steely glint entered Kit's eye. "I'll thank you to leave us alone! Just because you cannot find a woman of your own don't entitle you to come sniffing about my wife!"

"Kit!"

Dindie shrank aside, covering her ears. It was a wicked, an unpardonable taunt. Fiercely she bit her lip, fighting to regain control of herself. She heard Jamie go quietly out, heard Kit's laboured breathing. She had her back to him but his face was reflected in the shaving-glass on the wall. She saw the set of his jaw, the sulky line of his mouth and knew he was very angry. He was standing directly behind her but she was determined not to turn her head. Without warning he spun her round to face him, gripping her shoulders till they hurt.

"Just how long have you been allowing Jamie to make love to you?"

The biting sarcasm acted like touch-paper, inflaming Dindie to a fury as great as his own. How dare he chastise her with such arrogance? He who had least cause to assume outrage, with his arms still warm from that Spanish baggage! With full force she dealt him a resounding slap across the cheek, saying in choked tones, "I shan't tell you — but I wish it had been longer!"

"By Heaven, I'll teach you to answer back, my girl!" roared Kit, furious at this show of defiance. "I dare say you consider yourself grown up, flirting under my nose with Drummond. And, I don't doubt, with Harry Percy and Napier and the rest! We all know how that young milksop Burrard has been mooning over you since ever he arrived — has he been enjoying your favours too?"

Seizing her wrist he pulled her close. "Well, Madam, you may cease playing the coquette. If there is any flirting to be done you'll do it with me!"

"I should think you had occupation enough with your tempestuous Paquita!" she flashed back, too choked with anger and hurt to mind the consequences. She saw his expression alter but willed herself to hold his eyes, hearing her voice break on the words. "I am only your wife, Kit. I count for less than nothing with you — as much as any novelty of an hour, perhaps — and a vast deal less than your horse! But I — I did not dream you could so insult me as to reduce me to . . . to playing second fiddle to a Spanish whore."

"So it was you I saw running from the stables . . . " He gazed at her in silence. "Dindie, I — "

"Do not deny it, Kit, I beg you. It is enough that you have made me an object of pity and ridicule." Her eyes glistened with hot, shaming tears.

"I see no need for denial," he answered coolly. "For the Lord's sake, Dindie, I'm hardly a callow youth! What possible justification could there be for hurting you by mentioning a few stolen kisses?"

"You insult my intelligence if you expect me to believe that is all you enjoyed!" Her knuckles clenched white. "She had you burning with desire that day at the fair! Do you deny that you have lain with her, Kit — do you?"

"Since you ask, yes I have," he answered roughly, conscience pricking his anger to fresh heights. "Do you presume to deny me the right to enjoy what you yourself refuse to give?"

She turned from him, silent tears slipping unchecked down her face. He had made love with that creature . . . Dindie closed her eyes, but nothing could blot out the mocking pictures. In a voice barely above a whisper she asked, "M-More than once?"

"Does it matter?" He gazed at her a long moment. "I'm sorry you had to find out this way, Dorinda — but before you apportion blame reflect that infidelity cuts both ways. Your *Cavalier Servente* appears to have enjoyed considerably more in the way of reward than ever you have offered me!"

Dindie gasped. In that instant she realised how it was possible to love and hate simultaneously. She tried to hit him but he caught her small hands and held them, pinioning her against him with an amused laugh.

"I hate you, Kit!" she whispered tearfully, struggling against his superior strength. His grey eyes laughed down into hers, faintly mocking.

"You know very well you do not." A bellow of pain and fury broke from him as her teeth sank into his hand. "You bloody-minded little termagant! I'll teach you to bite!"

Seizing her ungently he wrenched down her bodice, exposing her firm, round breasts. "Once I would have taken you in love, wifeling," he breathed, "but you wish to play the timid virgin with me, whilst offering yourself to any other man who cares to show interest! In that case I claim what is my right!"

Crushing her mouth under his he forced her to the floor. Dindie screamed, helpless with terror as his hands tore aside her petticoats and she felt the heavy weight of his body on hers. Pain screwed through her, burning, relentless, strangling her protesting scream at source. The harsh thrust of his body exploded in a haze of agony and she submitted, gasping, to the white heat of his passion. The room spun into blackness and faintly through it all her mind registered, above Kit's harsh breathing and her own moans, something else — a compelling response deep within herself which she was powerless to check.

At length he rolled away from her and she lay motionless, mute tears wetting her cheeks, her body torn and bleeding. He had raped her, used her like a common harlot to gratify his lust without pity, without love . . .

Sobbing, Dindie attempted to stagger to her feet, hysteria choking her throat. Her lips were raw where he had bitten through them and her bruised body seared with pain stabbing as the agony which had gone before. The tattered remains of her skirts hung about her, a stained and bloodied rag. She felt besmirched, degraded.

Kit had started up, his face ashen. He tried to speak but his words were drowned by her own hopeless weeping.

"You hurt me . . . " She backed away, her voice high and thin. "Is this how you take your Spanish trollop, Kit? Does she enjoy being ravished like a — a s-serving wench in the hay?"

125

"Oh, God, Dindie – I never meant to harm you!"

He took a step towards her, his voice choked with shame and self-loathing. "I swear it, little love!"

"Don't touch me!" she whispered, whirling from him as he made to take her in his arms. "I cannot bear you ever to come near me again!"

The scorching pain doubled her up with a sharp intake of breath, but she strove to maintain a measure of dignity. Dragging her torn body to the rough ladder which connected the attic to the floor below Dindie knew, with hollow finality, that something living and precious had been extinguished within her.

Halfway down she rested her throbbing head against the wooden rungs, heedless of the raging of their host's wife who stood at the foot of the ladder incensed by her late screams. Nothing mattered — not Kit, not even her butchered, bleeding body, nothing. The pain in her head was taking over, blinding, insistent, blotting out even that other intimate distress. She clung to the rungs but darkness was closing in. Then she fainted.

9

Voices curiously far away penetrated Dindie's consciousness. She opened her eyes and thought she glimpsed the scarlet of Kit's uniform with its distinctive slashed buttonholes, then he was gone and she could not find him. Strange jumbled pictures chased through her brain, mingling with pain and blackness, then more pain. An arm was supporting her and she was vomiting into a bowl. It looked like Kit's arm but he had no face — only a sabre dripping blood hanging poised over one shoulder. She could feel the blood drip wetly on her own forehead and put up a hand, screaming as her fingers touched its macabre chill.

"You leave that wet compress be, Mrs Fane." Sadie O'Flynn's motherly cluck became blessedly recognisable.

"There, jewel." She adjusted the moistened linen on Dindie's brow. "Now, what does me favourite patient say to a drop of gruel? Sure, there's no finer recipe for invalids."

"Am *I* an invalid?" Dindie frowned, trying to recall events from the hazy mists of her mind.

"Have yez not been laid up them past three days of a fever? And was I not all but obliged to tie you down, the way you was threshing about and muttering nonsense at me?"

"This is a different room . . . " Dindie raised herself on one elbow with difficulty, wincing as stabs of pain shot through her. "I do not understand — "

"Bless you, we left Mayorga the day afore yesterday. This is Sahagun — and our brave lads has already had a wipe at them Frenchies! 'Tis a powerful victory, by all as me darlin' Paddy reports." She tucked the bedclothes warmly about Dindie. "We had you brought snug as sixpence in one of the waggons — but oh, them blizzards! Major Fane swore somethin' cruel at moving you but the doctor judged it safe, you not afther having the typhus like poor Lieutenant Penrice of the 15th."

"Kit . . . " Dindie lay back closing her eyes, his violation of her flooding back in all its bitter horror. She remained motionless, struggling to assimilate her feelings.

"I don't want to see him!" she whispered, seizing at Sadie's hands. "He — we had words." I cannot bear to face him, she thought wearily. Not yet.

"Now, there's no way to talk! Why, I nivver seed any man so distracted as the major. Tended you faithful, he has — wouldn't allow another soul near, not even to change your shift." Purposefully, Mrs O'Flynn brought a comb and hand-glass and pressed them into Dindie's reluctant hands.

Dumbly, Dindie gazed at her own reflection. The face which stared back, with its sunken shadowed eyes and swollen lips, was so unrecognisable that she could not bear to look more. What must the rest of me be like, she asked herself in anguish. Every movement precipitated that unfamiliar intimate ache deep inside. Fleetingly she wondered if Sadie suspected the truth? Hot shame burned Dindie's cheeks and she eased her bruised body involuntarily away from the other women, as though the terrible secret stood in danger of being exposed even through the rough Army blankets.

In silent agony she buried her face against one arm. Somewhere outside a muleteer was intoning the long nasal notes of a hymn to the Virgin Mary. A flurry of snowflakes drove relentlessly against the wooden window-shutters. Dindie suppressed a shiver. To her deadened brain its melting patter held a mocking chill, triumphant as Paquita's laugh which Kit's burning kiss had stopped in the convent at Mayorga.

*   *   *

128

Private Gabriel Flower whistled tunelessly as he stamped the snow from his boots in an effort to inject some warmth into his congealed limbs. He glanced across at the sprawling Benedictine building opposite with its row upon row of grilled windows, wondering idly why it was that headquarters was so frequently set up in monasteries and convents. Major Fane ought to be back soon. Flower had asked for him at the gate and been haughtily informed that the major was out with despatches and not expected back before noon.

Flower suppressed a yawn, watching his breath wreathe upwards in the frosty air. At least Sal would be warm in her stable, he thought. She was the one satisfying compensation to the rigours of campaign life, was Sal. Not that he was one to complain of Army treatment. More exciting than working the land back in his native Somerset. Some of the lads were rough and foul-mouthed, it was true, but at eighteen this merely added spice to the adventure. He had never been farther than Taunton in the whole of his life until now and consequently the regimental to-ing and fro-ing, the martial airs, the splendid accoutrements, the whole concept dazzled. And he could be with horses every day.

Horses were Flower's passion. He didn't mind being woken at dawn every morning when the clarion 'Stables' roused every dragoon to the care of his charger. Sal repaid his labours tenfold, with her soft eyes and silken mouth. The ritual three-hour session which followed on his uniform was less welcome. Whitening and pipeclay, blackball and spit and a thorough cleaning of his arms and equipment, all this before any man tasted his first meal of the day. Flower often wondered what officers ate for breakfast. Not bread dunked in a pint of beef broth, that was certain.

"Officers," Flannigan never tired of reminding him, with a sneer, "is pigs! Thinks of us as scum, they do! 'Tis a fact they cares more for them flea-bitten nags than they does of us! And I challenges any man to say different."

Nobody ever did. Flannigan was a trouble-maker and it did not pay to cross him. Flower, however, considered the regiment's officers a pretty fair bunch. He had been sorry when Captain Fane's promotion came through. Not snobbish and stiff-arsed like some, Fane was sympathetic, approachable, yet tough where bullying and indiscipline were concerned.

"A general's aide, is it?" Flannigan had taunted, when word of the captain's majority reached the ranks. "And what fancy qualities does that call for 'cept a hungry belly and the knack of stayin' on a horse at a split-arse gallop?"

No one had laughed. They perfectly knew, as did Flannigan, that in the thick of battle the exposed figure of the ADC was a prime target for enemy musketry and upon his skill in horsemanship rested the difference between victory and defeat. It was the aide who rode alone from brigade to brigade, the vital link carrying the orders of his commander, braving murderous artillery fire and frequently having his horse shot from under him.

Kit spurred his mare into a gallop, regardless of the fog swirling in a damp, impenetrable blanket around him. But for the looming towers of Sahagun in the near distance it was possible to imagine oneself riding over that soundless snow to the very edge of the world. Only yesterday he had covered this same stretch of ice-rutted track against a canopy of vivid blue sky, with the white ground sparkling like myriad stars and the trees lifting a tracery of exquisite beauty in homage to the new day. Dindie would like to have seen them, he knew.

Immediately, he cursed himself for the thought. Yet his mind refused to dismiss that fever-flushed countenance, the one hand flung upwards on the hard bed, the other lying securely in his own. Listening to her ramblings as the sickness mounted Kit had known fear and remorse, but nothing to equal the black disgust of himself. His own wife . . . his own sweet darling, who had given him her trust, whom he had vowed to cherish and protect. He could still hear her screams, that moment as her body went limp under him a torturing memory which reduced him to suicidal despair. Worst of all was the quiet despisal in her glance when he had finished, the numb, accusing eyes which said it all.

130

Had any other man so used a woman he would have been the first to brand him the veriest scum . . . Kit's anguished mind raced back to the horror-filled face of the regimental surgeon when he had looked up from examining Dindie.

"In God's name, Fane . . . what possessed you?"

"How badly is she hurt? Will she be — "

"I intend cupping her and shall prescribe bark to reduce the fever. As for her other injuries," his eyes swept over Kit coldly, "they will heal in time. The scars on her mind are a different matter."

Kit's face contorted and he turned away, close to tears. "She was a virgin," he whispered.

The surgeon stared at him appalled. "Then may Heaven forgive you, Major," he replied bluntly.

Kit clenched the reins tightly, causing his knuckles to stand out white. A dog ran across his path as he entered the town, bearing a string of sausages in its jaws with an irate commissary-driver chasing behind. There were so many similar cameos which he had found himself noticing of late. The intricate perfection of frost-flowers on glass; a basket of squirming new-born kittens in a Mayorga kitchen; the majesty of the snow-capped mountains of Leon rearing on the horizon against a backdrop of pink clouds; a certain amusing incident to relate . . . trivialities, yet significant because he wanted to share them with her, see her brown eyes glow in response — and could not. After all that had happened, brooded Kit, was there anything left to share?

"I count for less than nothing . . . " She had meant it too. His mouth drew together into an uncompromising line. How dare she believe such a monstrous untruth! Even before that final criminal act she was become a stranger to him, a disturbing little figure capable of exhibiting fires beyond his wildest imaginings. He could still feel the sting of her palm as it struck his cheek . . . This from the scrawny young cousin whose knees he had bandaged with court-plaster, whom he had taught to shoot down paper boats with horsechestnuts and play at bilbocatch! And there remained the final throat-sticking straw, the bitter discovery of her in Jamie's arms, her body pressed intimately close and her head thrown back with an abandon she had never revealed when alone with himself.

"Major Fane, sir."

Kit swung himself from the saddle outside headquarters and glanced round in enquiry. Private Flower stepped bashfully forward and saluted. In his hands was a small package, much creased and spattered with mud. This he held out, saying hesitantly, "They say Mrs Fane has been took bad, sir, an' — " He reddened, "I'd like fine if she'd accept this necklet to cheer her spirits. Been good to me, has Mrs Fane."

Kit accepted the package with a murmured word of thanks. "How do you mean — good to you?" he asked, slowly.

"Why, she been helping me with letters home, Major." Flower's uncertainty melted in his eagerness to talk of Dindie. "I never was no good at bookwork — never hardly went to the Dame School, see. But I wanted awful bad for my folks to know I'm well, an' Mrs Fane has wrote for me care o' the vicar."

Inside headquarters Kit unwrapped the twist of paper and stared at the cheap beads. They were of tawdry glass such as might be purchased from any street pedlar's tray. Yet Dindie would treasure them because they had been given with a spontaneity of heart by a common dragoon who prayed for her to get well. What has she had from me, argued Kit bitterly, but terror and pain. With a pricking of tears he stuffed the necklet into his fob pocket and went to report to the commander-in-chief.

Upon his return he found young Stanhope and Burrard in the library engaged in heated discussion with George Napier. From their exchange it was clear that Moore had dealt seventeen-year-old Harry a sharp ticking-off for something or other. Kit was in no humour for taking sides, however, and finding himself an empty chair subsided into it and drew pen and ink towards him with the intention of composing a letter to Lady Auden. If Dindie had been taken worse, he reasoned darkly, word would certainly be sent to him. But how to face her, what to say? . . . The truth was he could not bear returning to their lodging.

Kit sealed the letter with wax and listened idly to the drift of conversation at his elbow. He felt sorry for young Burrard. Moore had faults like everyone else and Kit had served under him at close quarters sufficiently long to observe that the chief was not adept at concealing his inner feelings. He was frequently given to obstinacy and at times Kit perceived a distinct lack of self-confidence, a clouding melancholy which sat heavily on the broad shoulders. Yet even in these emotional plunges into despondency or when something or other sparked him into vexation, one felt for the general rather than resenting his abruptness.

Young Harry Burrard stood in awe of Moore, was even now confiding to Napier that he found the chief disconcertingly aloof. Napier, who better understood the commander's varying moods, shook his black head emphatically.

"You're quite out, you know. It's simply that he don't hold with windbags and sycophants."

"Lord, *I'd* never try sucking up to him! Why, he scares me half to death."

"Serve you right for allowing him to fall into Colonel O'Lawler's clutches. Now that is just the sort of fellow he abhors — self-important Irish Johnnies who talk an infinite variety of nothing and keep him up half the night." Napier favoured his crestfallen young companion with an encouraging smile. "You'll learn."

"It's all well enough for you to talk, George — you are his favourite. Everyone knows that, " retorted Burrard, petulantly.

A flush stole over Napier's aquiline good looks but instead of the rebuke which Kit expected to hear he said, very quietly, "The chief has been like a father to me, Harry. I feel . . . close to him. It's not something easily explained. But I know this much — Moore is the best friend a soldier is ever likely to have. The very best," he added softly.

Somewhat embarrassed by this voicing of his inner feelings Napier rose abruptly and joined Kit. "I expect we shall be making another push on Soult tonight if this fog remains. Heard any whispers, Major?"

Kit shook his head. "No, but it *is* the chief's intention and he is not likely to be afforded a better opportunity for a night march. I'd wager it safe enough to commence packing up."

*　　*　　*

Dindie tossed listlessly on the hard bed. Her forehead burned again but sleep refused to come. Outside, the short winter day was fast drawing to a close, casting giant fingers of shadow over the room. Her ears caught the sounds of increased activity from the street below, a confused clamour of screeching wheels and muttered curses, interspersed with barks of command. She wondered what time it was. Sadie had left to give baby Jem his feed, leaving Dindie to re-live over and over her nightmare of grief and wretchedness.

At the sound of the door opening she murmured tiredly, "Sadie, is that you?"

The absence of reply forced open her eyes. Kit stood diffidently just inside the room, one hand resting on the doorknob. They stared at each other in silence.

"You . . . " The whispered exclamation stuck in Dindie's throat. She felt the blood rush to her cheeks under his penetrating gaze as the terrible silence lengthened.

Finally Kit dropped his glance, saying in muffled tones, "Dindie, I . . ." He gestured helplessly, his face drawn in anguish. "What can I say? . . .　　"

"Why should you try?" she answered, flatly. "We have nothing to say to each other."

She turned quickly into the pillow, biting hard into her fist to staunch the scalding tears which threatened to undo her.

"Oh, God, lovedy — don't turn from me! Do you imagine I am proud of what I did to you?" She heard his voice fail on the words and he sank heavily on the edge of the bed, burying his face in his hands.

134

At length he roused himself, and without looking at her said, in words scarcely above a whisper, "My crime is the foulest any husband can commit. The shame will go with me to my grave . . . and beyond." His hand reached out in a gesture of pleading then dropped to his side, as she drew back flinching.

"I deserve that." Their eyes met and she saw how much older he looked. There were lines deep etched round his mouth, and his eyes held a solitary suffering alien to them.

Dindie swallowed hard. In a low voice, she asked, "Does — does Sadie know?"

"No one knows, save you and I — and Surgeon Underwood who examined you," he answered quietly.

She felt his glance burn over every detail of her bitten lips. Could he, she wondered, begin to understand the depth of degradation she felt? Had it been the step-father whom she feared and detested who had ravished her, the sense of shame would have been no less marked — yet she might have lived with the knowledge. But it had been Kit, her own beloved Kit, the husband she loved and respected to the exclusion of all else, who had forced her into that intimate agony of humiliation and self-discovery.

Shock and pain had obliterated large tracts from Dindie's memory and those she did recollect caused her to colour hotly at the remembrance. Closing her eyes tightly she looked away, saying chokingly, "*Why*, Kit? . . . "

As if in the throes of some terrible inward struggle he raised his face to her. "I have no defence to offer save that I . . . I could not countenance the sight of you in another man's arms."

Dindie drew in her breath sharply. "You still believe I was unfaithful — that I was repaying you in your own coin for your — your dalliance with *her*?"

Kit made no answer. Rising, he strode to the narrow window and gazed grimly into the street. Her eyes followed him with stony calm. She would not cry more. It was as though a wall of ice was enclosing her heart. Nothing, not even his patent anguish, could pierce its shield.

135

"Do you intend to continue with the services of your professional doxy, Kit?" It was a subject she would not have dared voice a week ago. Now she might look him in the eye without flinching, numb to inward hurt.

His mouth hardened. "If I were to tell you the truth about that afternoon in the cloisters with Paquita, I doubt if you would believe me."

Dindie dragged her aching body into a sitting position and gazed at him calmly. "Strange, is it not, that you are happy to accept the evidence of your own eyes where Jamie and I are concerned, yet I am expected to make allowance for you and that lightskirt!"

At the scorn in her voice a glint of anger entered Kit's eyes. "Dindie, I did not go there to meet Paquita! If you must know, I had already determined to have nothing more to do with her."

"From what I could judge she appeared to be enjoying your fullest co-operation."

"We met by accident — or by her design, I know not which," he continued wearily. "I told her that I would not go on causing you hurt by furthering our association. She spat at me like a hell-cat and went for me with talons bared." His mouth twisted in a mirthless smile. "She called you all manner of intriguing names, as I recall."

"Go on," whispered Dindie, sensing his reluctance to continue. Kit shrugged.

"There is very little more to tell. Next thing I knew she had flung herself at me, leaving me in no doubt as to what she wanted." He gestured helplessly. "I do not expect you to believe me."

"No," she returned, coldly, "I do not believe it. What possible justification could she have?"

"I suspect," said Kit quietly, "that she perceived you before I did. She would not waste the opportunity to hurt you, Dindie."

"You are lying!" She turned away, trembling. "And what became of your laudable concern for me, Kit? Or did you tell yourself it would be of no consequence to indulge in one final fling? How do you imagine I feel, knowing you had made love with one of her sort only minutes before returning to — to . . . " Her lips refused to form the unmentionable word and she buried her face in her hands, choked with grief.

"I did not touch her, Dindie — I swear it!"

"But you would have — had I not interrupted," she accused hotly. "I dare say you will protest it is different for a man. Women are just so many conquests, are they not?" Her throat contracted painfully. "How do I rate, Kit? Or do wives not count?"

"*Dindie, stop it*! If I might undo every second of that accursed afternoon I would . . ." Abruptly, Kit turned again to stare down into the busy street.

Dindie gazed at him in silence.

"What do you see?"

"The past," he answered, with a dispirited laugh. "And the future. Our future — if we have one." He regarded her earnestly, with a something in his glance that penetrated her very heart. "Is there any hope for us together, Dindie?"

For a second that seemed like for ever their eyes strove. Then in a strangled voice Dindie heard herself whisper, "I — I do not know."

He came and stood humbly at the end of the bed.

"Wifeling . . . everything cannot be destroyed, surely?" When she made no reply he pleaded, in an outburst of anguished remorse, "Say you do not hate me, Dindie — I think I could not live with the knowledge!"

"I do not hate you, Kit," she answered quietly. "I — I am unable to feel anything for you at all, neither hate nor . . . " Swallowing down her tears, she faltered, "I am sorry."

"It might be best if we were to avoid each other's society for a period," responded Kit grimly.

"That is impractical and you know it."

"Would you have me be a reminder to you of this sordid business each time we meet?" He moved to the bed-table and measured out some drops from the bottle left by the surgeon.

"If that is laudanum I do not want it. It gives me bad dreams. I — I feel well enough to get up, I think."

Kit tipped the draught back into the bottle.

"As you please." He regarded her steadily. "We shall be moving out tonight, Dindie. I want your promise to remain with the women. The French are only twenty miles from here, at Saldaña."

Dindie's heart leaped painfully into life. "Moving out . . . you mean, going into action?" Trembling, she pressed a hand to her swollen lips, her eyes huge with apprehension.

"It's not official, but it is what the chief intends. After Lord Paget's rousing affair with the 15th Hussars, the men are wild for an opportunity to finish off Soult." He paused. "You have heard about our success at Sahagun?"

"Sadie mentioned something of it. Kit — " Her eyes fixed on his with an intensity hard to interpret. "Does that mean you will be in the fighting?"

"Certainly. Jamie, too," he added, with conscious cruelty. "Which of us would you rather have return to you, wifeling?" What prompted his deliberate taunt Kit could not explain but the flinching hurt in her face seared his conscience for long after.

Dindie gazed at him motionless, then in a proud voice remarked coldly, "I should like you to go, Kit."

"Not before I have your promise," he returned grimly. "Though you may despise me heartily, you are still my wife! I can no more dismiss your safety than forget to draw breath."

"Where else have I to go?" she responded wearily.

"I shall send Sadie to help you dress." Ignoring the despairing plea Kit turned to leave. It was then he remembered the beads Flower had given him.

Her pleasure in the cheap trifle irked his black mood into darker straits. God help me, thought Kit savagely. Matters have come to a pretty pass between us when I find myself consumed with jealousy over such a challenge as Gabriel Flower.

"Please inform Private Flower I shall be proud to wear his gift," whispered Dindie, caressing the winking glass with her forefinger.

"Would you wear any offering of mine so readily?" muttered Kit bitterly, and did not wait for her reply.

*   *   *

That same evening the infantry left Sahagun, marching in the confident knowledge that soon, very soon, they would have a battle on their hands. A thaw had set in and gutters overflowed into the slush-filled streets as they squelched past. It was going to be a fine Christmas after all and with any luck a New Year drunk on the spoils of victory.

But during that day of December 23rd reports had been coming in, both satisfying and disturbing, to the commander-in-chief. Heavy reinforcements were being rushed from Madrid to join Soult and the Marshal himself, realising the dire threat to his life-line, was positioning to attack. It was clearly time for Moore to make a get-away before his luck ran out.

Seated on his horse with rain trickling in rivulets from his oilskin, Sir John broke open and studied a despatch just arrived from General Romana via a Spanish peasant. George Napier, about to hand the chief his pistols, saw Moore's expression alter, then he was dismounting hurriedly and striding indoors with a crisp command to his aides to follow him.

As the convent bells tolled six o'clock Moore was already writing the necessary orders. He had succeeded in his intention. The might of Napoleon's armies was now bearing down upon his tiny force. A delay of even one more day must mean certain annihilation.

There could be no question now of the luxury of battle with Soult. The net was drawing tight, the coast his only hope of escape. Moore stared grim-faced at the evening sky. If the French reached the Esla fords before him it would be death or surrender.

James Drummond was halted with C Troop on a ridge near St. Nicolas, a small village on the road to Saldaña. Orders had been given for the Army to march in two columns under cover of darkness with the object of forcing the bridge over the River Carrion.

A number of the men who had been on duty non-stop during the past days were lying down beside their horses to gain a little sleep. Jamie had made himself a comfortable bed by spreading a truss of hay on the frozen snow. He closed his eyes but his thoughts were too active for sleep.

It was shortly after midnight when he saw Kit come spurring up to General Lord Paget, the cavalry commander. Jamie met his eye briefly then Kit turned away grim-faced. Within minutes the entire column had turned about and was retracing its steps with all speed along the rutted Sahagun road. It was Christmas Eve and the retreat was begun in earnest. Moore's bubble had burst.

10

THE CRACK OF pistols reached Dindie as she guided her tired pony through knee-deep mud and slush. More horses being shot, she reflected sadly. At Mayorga she had counted forty carcases in the main street. Since then the shooting of those horses and mules which were lame or incapable of keeping up had become a daily occurrence.

Before her the River Esla roared in spate. The water was rising fast. Through the driving rain she could see the first of the Baggage waggons approaching the ford. The thought of riding her pony into that foaming torrent was terrifying. Her insides lurched at the prospect. It had rained solidly for three days now ever since Christmas Eve and the familiar roads along which they had so lately come were now churned to black clay by the steady tramp of feet and the lumbering wheels of waggons and gun-carriages.

"There goes another village in flames, ducks."

Megs Baillie nodded from her perch aboard a crowded supply cart. Dindie wiped the streaming rain from her eyes and stared across the river. That makes the fifth today, she thought wearily.

How was it possible, she asked herself, that a responsible disciplined body of troops could in a few short days degenerate into lawless, drunken despoilers? Everywhere, as they followed in the wake of the infantry, fresh evidence met their eyes of the sorrowful degradation. Pent-up frustration, anger and disgust at General Moore's decision to retreat just when it looked as if they were set to thrash the enemy, resentment of the Spanish Army and its ineptitude, hatred of the local peasants who now spat in their faces and

141

barred doors and windows rather than offer accommodation — all had boiled over into an uncontrollable lust for revenge.

One village through which the women had passed presented a harrowing spectacle. Every house had been systematically gutted by fire. The wretched inhabitants could be seen rooting in dumb despair through the charred timbers that had been their homes. One old woman sat weeping piteously over a wooden stool, the only object she had managed to salvage from the flames. As the Baggage train passed through the streets eyes were turned in stony accusation and one man shouted, "*Viva los Franchaises!*"

Dindie's sense of shame and horror could find no expression. She had urged her pony on, tears pricking her eyes. In that moment she was ashamed of being English.

Thank Heaven the cavalry were continuing to maintain a civilised code of conduct. She wondered how they were faring. Now that the Army was in full retreat the women and children were meant to travel in the vanguard but the fierce pace and sleeting rain coupled with cold and fatigue had swiftly doubled the inevitable stragglers. Dindie could have kept up had she wished but Sadie was tiring quickly and her youngest boys crying with hunger and bewilderment. Mrs Baillie, too, was very near her time with hands and ankles so much swollen that she could barely walk.

Dindie knew from snatches of information gleaned en route that, together with the 10th and 15th Hussars, Jamie's regiment had been constantly engaged in sorties with enemy horsemen. General Moore was also travelling far to the rear with his staff, directing and encouraging his hard-pressed skirmishers and cavalrymen. Other than that Dindie knew cothing.

A splodge of mud from a puddle showered over her. Mechanically she wiped at her face. She had not seen Kit for three days.

Not that it would make any difference if she had. She prayed no harm might come to him, she wished him no ill but never could she forgive the numbing brutality of that day at Mayorga. She knew now it was quite finished between them. It had all been an illusion, the hurt entirely of her own making. He never professed to care, she told herself fiercely, never chose to regard you as anything more than a bed-warmer to be coaxed into compliance. You knew it, yet you continued to delude yourself, hoping . . .

"You well enough, ducks?"

Dindie scrubbed at her eyes. "Yes, to be sure." Resolutely she steeled herself to follow the high cart into the raging flood water.

*　　　*　　　*

Torrents of rain sluiced down, and the soggy plain of Benavente was littered with broken axles. Baggage-mules stuck fast in its quagmires also score upon score of stragglers and camp followers. By the following evening all the Army was safely across the Esla with the exception of the riflemen of the light brigade who formed the rearguard, and the engineers who were to work through the night to blow up the bridge farther down-river. Paget's cavalry, which had done sterling work in keeping its pursuers at bay since the commencement of the retreat, also remained behind to buy time.

Darkness was fallen when the hussars finally splashed their horses across the rapid swirl. A picket was posted near the bridge and the remaining regiments and horse artillery proceeded to Benavente where General Moore had established headquarters.

But discipline was breaking fast. The escalation of thieving and violence in the lust after alcohol appalled Moore. He was heartbroken to see the Army which he had led into Spain with such high hopes disintegrate so rapidly and so completely.

Even the sternest of the chief's critics had been shaken by the effect of his counter-order, reflected Kit gloomily, as he unclasped a penknife to mend some quills for the general within the latter's tent. When word of the decision came through on Christmas Eve the reaction had been extraordinary. Nothing could be heard on every side but the clang of firelocks thrown down in despair. It was a sullen, angry infantry that had filed out of Sahagun next morning.

It was understandable, of course, that they should feel betrayed. A confrontation with the French was what they had been promised. After the previous dash to their hopes, victory had seemed but a stone's throw away. Now . . . Kit's mouth tightened. Now they were mad for drink, firing their muskets into wine casks, passing off uniform buttons as English coin in order to obtain *aguardiente*, the powerful Spanish brandy that could knock a man blind drunk in five minutes.

He watched in heartfelt silence as Moore passed a weary hand over his face. Only a half hour before, word had reached headquarters that outside Benavente some men of the 52nd Regiment — Moore's very own 52nd whom he had trained at Shorncliffe to be an example to the Service — had thrown a fat prior of the monastery in which they were quartered headfirst into an enormous vat of wine because he had concealed it from them.

"The rearguard will not succumb, sir," ventured Kit, breaking the weighty silence. "Everyone knows the green-jackets will stand to the last man."

He had hoped to sound encouraging but the general remained sunk in spirits, his long fingers linked over the folding campaign table.

"It is a canker, Fane. A weakness and want of experience in certain officers which is charging the situation. It must not continue." He stirred, regarding Kit intently. "How does your wife fare, Major? This beggarly existence is wretched work in all conscience for one of her tender years. Is she reasonably quartered?"

"I understand the women are at the castle of the Duchess of Ossuna." Kit felt himself turn hot under the collar. Moore did not miss much. "We — have not had the opportunity to meet for some days, sir."

"Then it's above time you did. Leave those pens — I shall have need of them. And Fane," his glance softened, "be sure to tell your lady how profoundly we all miss her."

Eyes almost closing from lack of sleep Moore pulled a sheet of paper towards him to draft a stern General Order. Decisive action was called for to halt the excesses. In blunt terms he scribbled his concern at the gross misbehaviour of certain sections of the Army, mincing no words in his condemnation and levelling blame squarely with the officers in command.

It was not the stuff calculated to enhance a general's popularity, he reflected wryly, but he cared nothing for criticism in that moment. His tiny Army, already weakened by forced marches and with the French snapping at its heels, stood in grave danger of disintegration from within.

He read over what he had written, fingering the V-shaped dimple on his left cheek, legacy of a bullet which had ripped through at close range during the Helder campaign. Through the tent flap he saw that a thick fog had again blanketed the plateau. Reaching for his personal seal he studied it closely. The arms of Sir John Moore, K.B. — supported by a Light Infantryman and a Highlander, the last in grateful recognition of the two unknown kilted heroes who had dragged him to safety when he had fallen wounded at Egmont. Men of Huntly's regiment — Gordon Highlanders.

*　　　*　　　*

Dindie stood over a large cauldron in the kitchen of the castle at Benavente, busily chopping turnips to add to the watery soup which Sadie was preparing. Almost every door in the crumbling building had been torn down to fuel the fires. In the upper chambers priceless tapestries were being used as blankets by the uncaring troops, and the once elegant walls reeked of black smoke. Dindie's lower limbs were still numb from the icy river. She had discarded her sodden riding-habit and stood shivering in her petticoat, with the red Spencer jacket buttoned to her throat.

At the Irishwoman's tactful nudge she glanced up and saw Kit standing hesitantly in the kitchen doorway, watching her. He had evidently ridden some miles for he was soaked to the skin.

Slowly Dindie set down the knife but made no move towards him.

"Hello, Kit."

"I came to find out how you were."

His voice sounded awkward, strained. He came and stood beside her, fiddling with the knife which she had discarded.

"You made the crossing without mishap? I expect you used the ferry-boats."

"No." She indicated her sodden garments hung up to dry before the fire. She found her legs trembling.

"You mean — you actually rode across? Unaided?" Kit stared at her aghast. "You might have drowned!"

She forced a shaky laugh. "I was scared to death. But I managed to keep my nerve." She lowered her gaze, constraint taking over afresh. "Let me dry your sling-jacket, Kit."

She moved towards the fire but he stopped her with the urgency of his glance.

"Dindie, we must talk — " There was a desperation in his voice. Sadly, she shook her head. What was there to discuss?

"You go wid your man. I'll see to them greens." Sadie shooed her briskly away, adding shrewdly, "You can look afther Jemmy for me if you've a mind to."

Dindie picked up the baby and held him close, thankful to have some occupation. The silence was nerve-jangling.

Kit thrust a package towards her, saying gruffly, "For your birthday. I wanted you to have something . . . after all, we had a rotten Christmas Day." Embarrassment coloured his cheeks. "It's only a mantilla . . . "

She stared at the package, unmoved. He read her expression and added stiffly, "It's not meant as a peace-offering. I bought it in Salamanca, long before we — "

"Thank you," whispered Dindie. she had quite forgotten that today was her birthday.

Mechanically she patted the infant's back, her thoughts in turmoil. Jemmy kicked his tiny legs in protest and was promptly sick over her shoulder. Kit passed her his handkerchief in silence. As she took it from him he stiffened.

146

"Your wedding-ring — you are not wearing it." His mouth hardened in a bitter line. "Is it necessary to be so dramatic, Dindie?"

Resentment burned within her. Did he honestly believe she would shout their estrangement to the world in so vindictive a fashion? She was on the point of explaining, confessing to him that because of their scant diet her fingers were grown so thin that his ring no longer fitted. But his accusation dried the words in her throat.

Let him suppose what he pleased, she decided proudly. She had never truly been a wife to him. Wearing his ring would not alter the situation. Biting back an angry retort she watched him stride to the door. He pulled on his bedraggled cocked hat and turned.

"Keep on the move, Dindie," he commanded tightly.

"We cannot go any faster," she replied, without expression. "Are — are the French very close?"

Kit nodded grimly. "We shan't manage to hold them back much longer. If they should gain an inkling of how puny our numbers really are they will make every attempt to cross."

"But the river is rising every second! Surely they must realise how dangerous it would be to make pursuit?"

"They know we're running for our lives, Dindie. The Esla will be no barrier." With a last penetrating glance at her he went out into the black night.

* * *

Kit's prediction proved wholly accurate. Despite the thunderous waters the enemy cavalry managed to cross on December 29th. General Moore waited, as was his custom, until the bulk of his Army had left the town before following with his staff.

Kit was still busily packing up papers with John Colborne, in hopes of catching up the general on the road to La Bañeza, when he was startled to see a dragoon gallop past their tent, sabre unsheathed. Next instant Colborne's servant rushed in, shouting that the French had crossed the river.

Colborne's eyes gleamed. "Well, make haste! Take on my

baggage as fast as you can. Fane — this is a chance we cannot afford to pass up!''

Within minutes they were astride their horses and galloping towards the Esla. The charges laid by the engineers had blown up two arches of the bridge and its connecting pier but hordes of French cavalry were already braving the flood water. Waiting on the British side were Paget's hussars.

His lordship himself, looking every inch the dashing dandy of the general staff, galloped past Moore's two majors, twirling his famous moustachios and shouting, "You see, there are not many of them and the 10th will be here directly!"

Kit exchanged a brief glance with Colborne, then in common assent they immediately spurred their horses in pursuit. Kit felt exhilaration surge through his veins at the prospect of being back in action. This was what soldiering was about.

Paget took the men of the 10th and 18th Hussars to the edge of town and had them form under concealment of houses on a fold of ground where they would be positioned to surprise the advancing enemy horsemen. There he waited some thirty minutes with considerable cool until the French were just two miles from the river.

"Christ, look at that!" muttered Colborne.

Advancing in close column the French presented a daunting spectacle. There were between five and six hundred of them, chasseurs of the Imperial Guard. From his position of concealment it was just possible for Kit to see them forming into line on horses markedly superior in height to the small mounts of the Light Dragoons. Now they were extending in line, the black horse-hair streaming from their distinctive Roman-type helmets.

Those helmets, Kit knew, were lined with iron hoops and the thick brass chains under the chin would afford substantial protection against a sabre blow. He contrasted the soggy inadequacy of the hussar fur cap, stiffened only with pasteboard and capable of being cut down by the heavy French swords like so much cartridge-paper. About as much use in battle as Dindie's muff, he mused wryly, and twice as heavy.

148

Young Gabriel Flower felt his tongue stick drily to the roof of his mouth. In the intense cold his fingers were so benumbed that he could scarcely hold his sabre. In those interminable seconds before the charge a multitude of thoughts flashed through his mind. Of his mother baking bread in the familiar tiled kitchen back on the farm. Of his father, hands raw from the plough, grunting over ale and a pipeful of baccy at the long day's end. Honest God-fearing folk, they had neither of them wanted him to go for a soldier. He was their youngest and his yearning to step beyond the claustrophobic confines of crop yields and the price of corn to the real world was above their understanding.

Now, just one year later, facing those very realities over a tract of muddy plain, Flower's conviction was crumbling. He recalled September days harvesting in the fields with his brothers, warm sun on his back and the tingling scents of wood smoke and rich loam intoxicating his nostrils. Another two days, he brooded, and it would be New Year's Eve. Church bells, spiced ale and the warmth of family ties . . .

A tear trickled unashamedly down one side of his nose. On this bare Spanish plain outside Benavente home seemed very far away. He was just eighteen and very afraid.

Paget waited until the French, slowly but confidently pushing back the pickets of the 18th Hussars, had almost reached the fold of ground concealing his position, before giving the order to charge. As the two lines clashed head on there was a fierce struggle for some minutes. Shrieks of terror mingled with oaths and groans burst along the whole of the enemy front, the line broke under the bloody onslaught and prayers for mercy were drowned in the crack of pistols and the gurglings of the dying.

Kit witnessed one hussar lop off the arms of a Frenchman with the ease and neatness of slicing through a sausage. Sabres flashed, bloodied from tip to hilt. One man fell, his head split down the middle. In some places Kit found it impossible to press forward because of the obstructing mounds of writhing horses and bodies intertwined in hopeless constriction.

Jamie saw the adjutant fall, badly mauled in the face. He made to go to his assistance but was waved on fiercely. So fierce was the clash that in the misty drizzle it was difficult to tell friend from foe.

Private Flower struggled to keep his mare on her legs. His sword-arm had been pierced and the red-hot pain left him barely able to defend himself. A severed hand thrown up by a drumming hoof landed on Sally's mane. He heard his own curdling scream, tried desperately to rid himself of the gruesome object and fell heavily in the churned snow, sobbing hysterically. Through the driving rain a charger bore down. Flower glimpsed the flash of steel upraised to destroy him and screamed in terror.

"Flower! Good God, lad — is that you?"

Shaken, Kit lowered his sword. "I took you for a Frenchman! Get up this instant!"

Flower continued to sob uncontrollably. Kit leaped from the saddle and still grasping his charger's bridle-rein dealt the young private a hard blow across the face.

"Do you want us both to be trampled to death? Get on your horse at once, do you hear?"

Dazedly Flower complied. Kit flung himself back into the saddle and set spurs to his mount, bellowing for Flower to follow. He had seen hysterical youngsters go to pieces in their first charge too often not to know that shock treatment was the only cure.

"Make for the rear! I'll cut a path for you. And keep your head down or you'll lose it!"

Slowly but relentlessly the chasseurs were pushed back towards the river. Kit was struck in the hand by a carbine shot but managed to urge his horse to safety, where he stumbled to the shelter of a low wall, bleeding heavily.

"Fane! Where did you appear from? . . . Good Lord, you're bleeding like a pig!"

"Cease fussing, Ned — it's only my hand, dammit." Kit subsided into the mud, sweating with exertion but thankful to have fallen in with some former comrades from the 18th Hussars.

"I suspect the bullet must still be lodged — fingers won't move."
He lay back grinning through his pain. "Well, give us a swig from
your confounded liquor-flask."

Utter weariness was seeping over him and the chilling wet
congealing his limbs came as relief, blotting out the throb from his
bloodied hand. Around him corpses and wounded littered the
slushy ground, staining it crimson. As he waited for a medical
orderly to come up Kit made out several of their own men swearing
with pain, yet to his mind the French prisoners looked worse off.
Through his faintness he heard the drum of hooves and recognised
Daniel Flannigan. Deliberately the Irishman rode up to one badly
injured French dragoon, sabre brandished. The man screamed for
mercy, raising himself with difficulty and tried to strip off his
cross-belts to show that he surrendered.

"Flannigan — *no!*"

Kit's hoarse shout fell on deaf ears. With a crashing stroke the
Irishman brought the sword down, cleaving his victim's skull.

"You bastard!" Scarcely able to speak for horror and rage Kit
stared from the young Frenchman's bludgeoned head to the grinning Flannigan. Brains and splintered bone spewed through the
pumping, sticky mess which had been the lad's skull. Kit turned
away vomiting.

"Why, if it's not yourself, Major." Flannigan wiped his sabre,
fingering the leather grip with satisfaction before replacing it in its
scabbard. "Sure I don't like to let a day pass widout cutting down a
Frenchman. 'T would have been a sin to suffer such a favourable
opportunity to slip."

Kit watched the private wheel his horse and gallop off. Revulsion and fury at his own helpessness had overset his pain so that he
failed to see a movement behind him. That same instant a shot rang
out, there was a rending scream and a French prisoner toppled
over the wall doubled up in agony.

Shaken, Kit saw Jamie regarding him silently, his pistol still
smoking from the shot.

"Save your gratitude," Jamie spoke abruptly. He indicated the twitching corpse of Flannigan's victim. "I'd have done the same for him if I had been close enough. Where's your horse?"

"Lord knows. Jamie . . . " Kit swallowed hard. Their eyes met briefly, warily. "Thanks."

He regarded the pumping bullet wound in his hand with fixed preoccupation, saying quietly, "You could have let that fellow kill me. Why didn't you?"

Jamie pulled off the muslin cravat at his neck and shrugged. "Dindie would be mine for the asking then — is that what you're implying?"

"Well, you are in love with her." Kit looked at him hard. "I've not been altogether blind these last weeks."

Jamie paused only fractionally in fashioning the cravat into a makeshift bandage and sling. "Aye," he returned, briefly. "I do love her. And I'll take her from you if I can."

They stared at each other in strained silence.

"Then why in God's name did you save my life?"

"Because I'm a fool." Jamie knotted the sling securely behind Kit's neck. "Put your good arm round my shoulder," he commanded. "I'm taking you to the dressing-station."

*   *   *

General Moore might never have learned of his staff's scrap with the enemy if Lord Paget, when reporting the affair to him at La Bañeza, had not chosen to add, with a wink, "But there's your military secretary. He was there, and knows all about it!"

Moore's brows snapped together. Turning to Colborne who stood with stricken expression, he declared sternly, "Oh! You there, were you?"

Colborne groaned silently. His co-partner in the action was still having his wound dressed. There was nothing for it but to carry the can alone.

Without doubt more would have been said on the subject had they not been interrupted. A wounded French officer magnificent in a sodden uniform of scarlet, gold, olive and white was ushered in. He turned out to be Bonaparte's favourite aide-de-camp General Comte Charles Lefebre-Desnouettes, the nephew of the Empress Josephine and commander of the cavalry of the Guard.

This was a rare feather in the cap but Moore's inward satisfaction was nowhere evident in the courteous reception he afforded his guest. Immediately young James Stanhope was despatched to bring warm water and with his own hands Moore cleaned the French commander's head wound. He also furnished some dry under-linen of his own, for the unlooked-for arrival was in a sorry state.

His charger, it transpired, had baulked at crossing the Esla a second time. Moore readily sympathised with the younger man's dejection. Not merely was it the acute sense of shame which stigmatised as a prisoner-of-war. Bonaparte himself had apparently been following the action from the heights and the Emperor never forgave the unfortunate.

As their guest went off to change Sir John, looking thoughtful, drew his military secretary aside.

"Would it be right, do you think, to ask our friend for a written promise not to escape?"

"On no account, sir!" Colborne looked shocked by the suggestion. "If you recollect, we had just such a case in Sicily. It would be construed as no end of an affront. Devilish touchy, these Continentals."

"Perhaps so." Moore's flicker of amusement nevertheless held a deeper concern, but he acquiesced. "I am glad you told me this. Of course I will not ask."

Moore's uncanny perception of human nature caused him to be not altogether happy with his decision but sheer politeness demanded it. At dinner Lefebre-Desnouettes appeared in a uniform of even more splendid proportions. His personal baggage had been sent for under a flag of truce, yet he still looked wretched. How was he to feel comfortable? His sword had been taken away.

The commander-in-chief, enquiring courteously if his guest now had everything he needed, saw the Comte glance crestfallen at his naked side. Without a word Moore unbuckled his own finely worked sabre and handed it to his adversary.

Astorga was reached by the leading divisions that same day. When Moore's rearguard stumbled wearily into the town on December 30th accompanied by their general they found it bursting with troops, Spanish as well as British, for Romana's stragglers had been pounced upon by the French, causing the bulk of his army to fall back on Astorga. The alternative route through which Moore had requested Romana to make retreat was blocked by snow and the Spanish commander had no option but to swell the already congested British line with his survivors.

The enemy was now a mere fifteen miles behind. And as General Moore, sickened and grieving over the escalating excesses of his army, prepared to call a council of his senior staff he knew, as his drunken, insubordinate infantry could not or would not realise, that an enemy more deadly still waited in the screaming white mountains above the town.

11

Kᴉᴛ sᴡᴏʀᴇ ꜰᴜʀɪᴏᴜsʟʏ, fighting to press his horse through the choked streets of Astorga. Everywhere, it seemed, drink-maddened marauders were breaking down the heavy doors of the *bodegas* and as the wine cascaded into the gutters it was scooped up in army shakos and drunk greedily.

"Santa Maria!"

The terrified scream pierced the night air. A chair crashed through the gaping hole where a door had been battered down and the woman's hysteria subsided to a hopeless sob. Hunger and suffering were forgotten as the wine, chased down with ration rum, turned soldiers into snarling animals, ready to fight their Spanish counterparts for possession of artillery mules, hurling insults and threatening the sobbing townspeople who barred their way.

Hell, thought Kit appalled, held nothing in comparison. Against the black sky fires flared, mingling acrid smoke with the thick fog that filtered through the narrow, crowded streets. On every side passageways were blocked by panic-stricken inhabitants fighting to escape over jam-packed bullock carts and baggage waggons. In one chapel he had seen cavalry horses tethered to a brazen font filled with oats and another troop-horse irreverently secured to a massive image of the Holy Virgin. Above the roar, chattering musket shot could be heard and a bugle's staccato blast.

"Get back to your billets!" roared Kit, firing his pistol into the air. Where the deuce had the provost marshal's men got to? He did not much care to be isolated amongst this hostile scum.

"Have you forgotten how to behave like men?"

"You mind your ain bluidy business!" A kilted highlander grappled with his horse's bridle-rein. "They Papes can burn in their ain muck-middens. They're naethin' but traitor malten-bellies onyhow!"

As if to underline the point a house opposite burst into flames, the crackling timbers roaring into the roof with frightening speed. A burning window ledge crashed into the street, narrowly missing Kit as he struggled with the Scotsman. Suddenly he felt himself being dragged from the saddle and a fist ploughed into his stomach, crumpling him in agony into the black slush.

"There's one for meself, Major! And there's another for your bloody fatigues!"

Flannigan's boot dug viciously into his ribs. Through a daze of pain Kit recognised the hate in the private's face. Flannigan's eyes stared red and murderous through the grip of drink. He had lost his dolman and his shirt hung in ribbons.

"Sure I can't make up me mind which of yez I loathe the most — Tom Jackson or you, Major Bloody Fane!"

"Ach, leave him, Paddy — let's find oorsel's a wumman."

Kit stared unwaveringly at the Irishman. "It was you who framed Jackson . . . I knew I was right!"

"Ah, you're the clever one, to be sure. But yez didn't tumble 'twas Dan Flannigan as pointed your darlin' wife to the stables where you was takin' your pleasure!"

A further kick from Flannigan's boot doubled Kit on his side. Faintly he heard the private's mocking shout as the pair were swallowed into the crush.

*   *   *

Inside the crowded *posada* Dindie listened with mounting apprehension to the terror outside. Through the swirl she could see flames shooting high into the night. The stinking fumes permeated even into the *posada*. Was it possible that this unfolding chain of horror could, in so short a time, have turned her world to ashes?

156

She recalled with an ache that golden hour spent in Salamanca Cathedral with Kit. Was it really only three weeks ago?

Hunger gnawed her insides. She had not eaten since yesterday morning and counted herself fortunate. For some days now they had been very irregularly furnished with provisions. Rations were supposed to last three days but she knew from Jamie that the cavalry was sometimes four or five days together without receiving any and were forced to forage for themselves.

The women of their party were now fallen so far behind that they were dangerously exposed. Sickness was prevalent and some women had already been forced to drop out altogether. Rifleman Harris of the 95th had secured for her own group a portion of emaciated bullock, one of the many wretched pack-animals that had collapsed from exhaustion. A month ago Dindie would have been horrified even to consider the prospect. Now, food from whatever source was acceptable.

The din from the streets was increasing. Shivering, she returned to the smelly corridor where most of the wives lay huddled with their littles ones trying to snatch a few hours sleep. Feet and ankles were raw and bleeding. Many women were barefoot. Dindie's own shoes had been taken away by John Harris, who was a cobbler to trade. He had promised to mend them if he had time, which was doubtful. Her pony had gone lame and she had trudged the last miles to Astorga, forcing on her aching limbs until her soles were worn quite through. In her ears the shouts and clash of steel had sounded faintly, emphasising with dread clarity the nearness of the French as they harried the rearguard.

Dindie found herself a space on the hard floor and lay down, weariness washing over her. Time meant very little. She had no idea what day of the week it was. Each hour was geared to survival; hunger and dysentery placed her on an equal footing with the other wives and with them she took her turn at cooking meals and at emptying the communal bucket in which they relieved the needs of nature. Always at the back of her mind rose the chilling memory of those rotting corpses at Sahagun. On Christmas morning the Army

157

had retraced its steps over the battleground and there she had seen them, the mutilated decaying corpses being gorged by vultures and dogs. Spanish peasants had already stripped the bodies clean and in the harsh morning light dismembered limbs protruded grotesquely from their pall of crackling ice. Dindie had hardly slept since.

A commotion farther down the corridor roused her. Letty Harper, whose husband was a chosen-man in Captain Hay's troop, was in vigorous argument with the gypsy Paquita. Dindie had not seen much of the dancer lately and was glad of it but she had heard from others that the girl had twice fainted on the Astorga road.

"You're a dity-mouthed liar, so you are!" Letty was shouting. "If you must pin the blame on one of our men, go choose some as would have you!"

"*No escucho!*" screamed Paquita, pushing the other aside. "*Preñada* — I tell you!" Her eyes flashed spitefully over Dindie who was half-sitting up and regarding her in silence. Advancing with an unpleasant smile she stood over Dindie and unleashed a tirade of Spanish.

Dindie's colour changed. "What does she say?" she whispered, yet the few words she had understood gripped ice-cold at her heart. Letty Harper snorted contemptuously.

"It's more than a Christian ought to repeat, dearie. Them's not fit words to be listened to."

"Tell me!"

Letty glared at the sulking Paquita.

"Says she's been sewed up. Pregnant."

She looked embarrassed. "Mrs Fane — I hardly likes to say this and it's got to be a wicked lie — I know that, but . . . she's blaming the major for it."

Dindie sucked in her breath sharply. Burning passion brought her to her feet instantly, revulsion of the girl and what she stood for firing her to storm, "You — you shameless bitch! How dare you accuse my husband! Your child could be *any* man's . . . "

Paquita's eyes narrowed. With a furious cry she sprang at

158

Dindie, nails drawn. Dindie backed away and in that second she saw a stiletto flash in the girl's hand. The other women fell back screaming as she wrestled desperately to turn the deadly blade, keep it somehow above her head.

A sob of fear broke from her. Her arms were tiring and the gypsy girl was strong, with an animal wildness in her which Dindie could not match. Down flashed the knife. Somehow — she would never know how — Dindie's foot slipped, knocking them both off balance. Paquita screamed, a piercing, curdling scream that shattered the night.

"My God! . . . You've killed her!"

Dazed with shock, Dindie slowly sat up. Paquita was lying in a pool of blood with the knife buried in her heart.

Dindie's hand flew to her mouth but the scream refused to come. Figures were rushing from everywhere, women screaming, voices — everywhere voices. Trembling she leaned against the wall. Her arm was gashed and blood soaked her skirts. Paquita's or her own — she had no way of knowing.

God, what had she done? As though drugged she stumbled to the stair-rail and grasped at it. This could not be happening! Someone was calling her name, She swayed, felt herself held in strong arms and looked into Jamie's ashen face.

"I slipped, Jamie . . . " she whispered. "I — I did, truly! Oh God, Kit will never believe me . . . "

Sobbing hysterically she slumped against him, jumbled incoherent words spilling from her. Jamie held her tight, shouting for someone to bring some wine to revive her and made her sit on the stair, wrapping his coat about her shoulders.

"It was an accident, Jamie!" she wept over and over. "How could I possibly k-kill her? I hardly knew her."

"Drink this," he commanded, forcing a glass to her lips. "Now listen well. There's none to blame for what has happened. And you've not killed her."

She stared wildly at him, her mouth trembling on a sob.

"They are taking her to be treated now."

159

Dindie uttered a little moan, relief flooding over her. Jamie sat himself next to her on the stairs and gathered her close, straining to catch her hiccuped sobs.

"She said it was Kit's b-baby." The words were barely audible. Jamie stiffened, his face registering disbelief.

"Dindie, that's impossible! You know it is."

"Why is it impossible?" she choked. "She has been his — his strumpet all along!"

"Think, lass," he urged. "Do you honestly suppose Kit is the only man she's been dallying with? Besides, he wouldn't be such a fool as to — "

"He admitted of it quite openly . . . " Her voice shook. "What am I to do? He — he will never believe the truth . . . I know it." She clutched at his hand.

"Jamie, if you care anything for me — "

"I love you," interrupted Jamie, quietly. "And if anything were to happen between you and Kit I should want to care for you always. I think you know that already."

He took her face and kissed it gently. "Now my dear, we had find your husband."

She felt herself picked effortlessly up in his arms and carried downstairs past the silent, curious faces gathered about the piazza.

Wrapped warmly before the charcoal *brasero* in Jamie's lodging Dindie waited in dread for Kit's return. Jamie had been gone more than twenty minutes. His words rang in her ears, breaking through the horror with merciful warmth. Jamie loved her — but she was bound in marriage to Kit who did not, and Paquita's blood was still warm on her hands . . . She closed her eyes tightly, suddenly afraid.

The house was full, with men of assorted regiments, both officers and rankers, sharing the meagre comfort. Through her semi-consciousness conversation drifted in confused murmurs. Word was just received that the Army was to diverge at Lugo. One division under General Fraser with the two light brigades

160

would branch off on the Vigo road and General Moore would take the main Army on to Corunna.

Kit's arm shook her back from drowsiness. His lip was cut and bleeding and his uniform black with mud. He brushed aside her startled exclamation at the sight of his heavily bandaged left hand.

"Never mind that now!" He seized her shoulder urgently. "Dindie — whatever made you do it?"

She stared back motionless. There was a frightening chill about his manner. Surely he understood? She dropped her gaze, saying flatly, "She is carrying your child."

Kit's grip tightened painfully.

"You . . . honestly believe that?" he muttered.

"You are her lover!"

He stared at her, stony-faced. "Not any longer. Paquita died a few minutes ago. I still cannot believe it . . . "

Shock knotted Dindie's throat. The girl was dead, after all. She killed me first, her heart screamed in silent agony. That day in the cloisters at Mayorga . . .

In that instant Dindie made her decision.

*   *   *

As the remaining hours of 1808 slipped away the rearguard left Astorga, following the long ragged chain of the Army that inched through hissing sleet into the harsh mountains. Ice crackled underfoot and stabbing blasts of wind knocked men off their feet as they slipped and struggled up the twelve-mile pull of white waste that formed the Monte Toleno ridge, sinking up to the armpits in snowdrifts from the weight of their knapsacks.

In front the infantry toiled, bent double like scarlet snails with each man's musket slung round his neck to keep the muzzle dry. Hunger and despair stared from every eye and silence hung over their ranks, broken only by a curse or the pain-maddened scream of a straggler lying down in the snow, too weak to carry on.

Accompanied by his staff, Sir John Moore followed the terrible cavalcade riding at the rear with his Reserve, yet even his own

161

encouraging presence could effect little impression on spirits numbed by starvation and disease. Typhus was now rampant, having been spread through the British lines by the gaunt wretches of Romana's patriot army. But the Spanish winter was already accounting for still more lives. No matter where one looked in this desolate landscape Death stared back.

At Astorga the empty magazines had been a bitter blow. Moore had counted upon replenishing the Army's scant supplies, realising full well that the next Commissariat store was fifty miles farther on at Villafranca. The bungling incompetence of this most vital service was unbelievable. Staffed as it was by inexperienced officers who had never before been faced with providing supplies on so vast a scale the imperfect system had collapsed utterly at Benavente.

For fear of their falling into enemy hands thousands of shoes and blankets had been brought out of store and burned by over-zealous or panicky Commissariat officers before either the Spanish or British Army had been fully re-equipped. Hundreds of men now trudged barefoot who might otherwise have received stout foot-wear. Moore's jaw tightened in frustration. It was needless, inexcusable negligence.

The drunkenness and violence continued to plague the march at each halt but a frightening number of stragglers had refused or were incapable of rejoining their corps. Too drunk to move they must, he knew, be soon overtaken by the French cavalry who would not scruple to butcher them in their helplessness. Unfounded rumours that a stand would be made at Astorga had exploded in fury and disgust when it became apparent that no such wipe at the enemy could be afforded. There was no time even to stop in humanity's name to help the sick and dying. The only hope for his tiny army was to push and prod it relentlessly forwards, forcing the pace to reach Villafranca where, in the high mountains beyond, they would be little more than a hundred miles distant from the sea at Corunna or Vigo.

Outside Combarros some men of the Reserve were getting under arms when a dragoon rode up. An officer who had taken to one of the light carts suffering from fatigue called out weakly, "Dragoon, what news?"

"News, sir? The only news I have for you is that unless you step out like soldiers, and don't wait to pick your steps like bucks in Bond Street of a Sunday with shoes and silk stockings, damn it, you'll all be taken prisoners!"

"Pray, who the devil are you?"

"I am Lord Paget. And pray, sir, who are you?"

The officer turned pale. "Captain Donovan of the 28th, my lord."

"Come out of that cart directly! March with your men, sir, and keep up spirits by showing them a good example!"

Gabriel Flower heard this sharp rebuke and groaned in resignation. What was the use of running so fast? If the French didn't kill them first the march would, for certain. He hadn't tasted a decent bite in his belly for four days. Sergeant Baillie had suggested sucking a piece of leather for nourishment. Flower had tried it but the taste upon an empty stomach had made him violently sick. There was an aching rheumatism across his shoulders and he had not shaved since Benevente. Many officers and men now sprouted beards of several days' growth.

Sally was tiring fast. The little mare had fallen several times on the ice and she was so thin her bones stuck out. Some of the lads had already been forced to shoot their chargers. A lump rose in Flower's throat. If he had to do away with Sal they had as well take his life too.

"No sign of Flannigan yet, lad?"

Major Fane brought his horse alongside, shading his eyes against the harsh glare of the snow. Flower shook his head. The Irishman had been missing since Astorga. Blind drunk or more like hiding out after that booting he'd given the major. Flower frowned. Striking an officer was a capital offence. It'd be the firing squad or the rope if they caught him, for sure.

"I don't have a vendetta against Flannigan, if that's what you imagine," said Kit quietly, glancing at the private. "But I had

163

sooner see him face a fair trial for his stupidity than think of him spiked at the end of a French sabre."

"I've not seed him, Major, honest!" gasped Flower, drawing a strangled breath as icy hail snarled into his face.

Kit shrugged acknowledgment and turned up the collar of his oilskin. His feet and legs were slightly frostbitten and so much swelled that he had not been able to remove his boots for two days. Ahead a Baggage waggon was stuck fast in a drift. Women were lifting down crying children from the top and preparing to continue on foot. Reining in, Kit recognised his wife endeavouring with difficulty to support Megs Baillie. The sergeant's wife was gasping in pain, her face grey.

Struggling in face of the raging hailstorm to keep the heavily pregnant Megs on her feet Dindie all at once felt the burden lifted. Kit's voice urged her to bring up his horse and she obeyed blindly, hardly able to see where the animal stood.

"Is she very bad?" demanded Kit quickly.

"The baby has started." Dindie's voice sounded scared. He detected it and said in firm tones, "How frequent have the pains been coming, Dindie? Think — it's important."

"The last was under ten minutes ago."

"As often as that!" Startled, Kit bent over Mrs Baillie's sweating face. "Can you make it to Bembibre?" he asked, urgently. "It's only a couple of miles from here."

"Little perisher ain't prepared to wait that long, Major." Megs gasped sharply as another contraction screwed through her. "Fetch Arthur . . . I wants me man! 'Urry, ducks," she pleaded. "This 'ere parcel's in a bleedin' haste."

Kit tossed off his oilskin and spread it on the snow.

"She's too far gone to risk proceeding farther, Dindie. Stay with her — I'll fetch Sergeant Baillie and Sadie O'Flynn. Lord knows she has had enough experience of this sort of thing. Where is she?"

"In front somewhere. Kit — what shall I do if — " She felt his hands grip hers reassuringly.

164

"Don't worry. I shall be back within minutes. Keep her warm — you will find a blanket under my water-deck."

As she waited with Megs in agonised suspense, Dindie still felt the pressure of his fingers and knew a glimmer of comfort. It was their first real contact since that horror-filled night in the inn at Astorga. An impregnable barrier of ice was grown up between them, a hostility of silence that deadened all feeling. Paquita in death was more hauntingly tangible a presence dividing them than ever she had been in the flesh.

Dindie felt the girl's blood heavy on her conscience. Not once had Kit mentioned the incident since but his face was etched with a grimness far beyond anything which had gone before. Sometimes she caught him regarding her with a long, unfathomable gaze which twisted her insides. When he sought her out at the day's end it was to share his rations with her, or to satisfy himself that she was well. If he had accused her outright, struck her even, she might have been better able to accept his condemnation but he did none of those things, and Dindie knew with terrible finality that what she had done would never be forgiven. Even his vile ill-usage of her, the scars of which she still bore, must pale in comparison.

But Dindie had her plan. She could not bear to go on as now. It had been bad before but . . . she swallowed painfully. Jamie would help her, she knew. Her mind was made up.

"I can't find Sadie." Kit knelt beside Megs, worry and frustration chasing his countenance. "Dindie, you will have to help me. Just do exactly as I bid you."

The makings of a smile sparkled his eyes. "I have never attemped this sort of game before, Mrs Baillie. But I have delivered foals — I suppose it's the same principle."

"My God, Major, you never was one to mince words." Arthur Baillie put an arm round his wife and looked nervously at his former commander. "Not my line of country, this ain't — but if there's anything I can do . . ."

"Just soothe her, man. Get her to relax if you can. Dindie, bring the horses closer. She deserves some privacy."

Dindie led her pony into a sheltering angle next to Kit's mount. Sergeant Baillie's horse had already foundered some way back. The numbing tiredness under which she had laboured earlier was dispelled magically. Kit was relying upon her. He had discarded his jacket and was rolling up his shirt-sleeves but was experiencing difficulty because of his wounded hand. In silence Dindie knelt beside him and secured the cuff for him. She could feel the tenseness of his muscles under her fingers.

"Good girl." He flashed her a grateful smile. "Now Dindie, attend carefully and do just as I instruct."

*   *   *

"By Jasus, Mr Hills!" Jamie heard a rifleman ask his officer in breathless exasperation. "Where the devil is this you're takin' us to?"

"To England, McLachlan," was the melancholy reply. "If we can get there."

If, indeed, thought Jamie grimly, urging his tired mount with an encouraging pat. Never had he witnessed such appalling congestion. As far as one's eye could see the road was littered not only with their own abandoned stores and ammunition waggons but now swollen to chaotic proportions by coaches and calashes bearing fleeing Spanish families and their servants intent upon reaching Corunna and Ferrol.

They had already passed several carts filled with sick and wounded. Poor wretched devils who had not a hope of making it to the coast and knew it. Jamie doubted if they would survive another freezing night in these mountains. Almost certainly the French would end their suffering eventually.

To the left another village was burning steadily. Each fresh sign of devastation by the leading regiments redoubled within him a shame and anger that surprised even himself. All restraint was gone. They evidently believed there was nothing to lose. Death stared before and behind in this white wilderness. All along the terrible winding track the carcases of bullocks and mules littered the snow: half-hidden by ice-covered boulders, carried along in the rushing streams, blocking the rough bridges. Every time an animal dropped down from sheer exhaustion a party of soldiers would be detailed to drag its load by turns. When they too succumbed to weakness and hunger the stores were abandoned.

Hundreds of pounds worth of supplies and ammunition had already been dumped in this fashion. There was no alternative. In front Jamie recognised General Moore riding with Colonel Anderson and Lord Paget, the latter sporting a green eye-shade above his moustachios to counteract the effects of snow blindness. What must Moore's feelings be, wondered Jamie. Surely he must despair of their ever surviving the two hundred and fifty miles across the Galician mountains. His only bitter consolation must be the knowledge that Bonaparte's Army was also experiencing the full horror of suffering, disease and death. The Emperor's soldiers must also be forced to halt, take shelter, snatch an hour's sleep.

Rubbing the weariness from his eyes Jamie rode on in fixed preoccupation, but no matter how he steeled himself to resist he found his thoughts turning to Dindie. God, what a mess it all was! He had noticed the scratch marks on Kit's face, knew beyond doubt from Dindie's impassive manner that something of dire finality had transpired after he had left them in the lodging at Mayorga. Yet at any broaching of the subject her lips would press together in silent appeal, leaving Jamie to reproach himself for his insensitivity.

At the remembrance of that hysterical, tear-stained little face which he had kissed into quiet after its ordeal in the *posada* his resolve hardened. He was glad that he had declared his feelings at last, glad that she knew. Whatever happens from now on, decided Jamie grimly, she has the certainty of my protection. And if there is the least chance of our finding happiness together I mean to grasp it with both hands.

12

"IT'S A BOY." Kit bent over Megs Baillie, his voice quietly excited. "And he has a shock of black hair that would be the envy of Samson!"

Megs lay back in the snow, elation chasing the deep-pitted exhaustion from her face.

"Didn't I tell you, Attie? Knew it by the way 'e kicked."

The sergeant grinned his relief and delight and they held hands, oblivious to anything but the intimate magic of the moment. Dindie wiped the sweat from Kit's brow, marvelling at the gentleness in those strong fingers, the sureness of his every movement. He motioned for his sabre and she handed it over, watching in silence as he severed the birth cord which she had already tied off under his instruction with strips torn from her petticoat.

Immediately the infant's weak cry broke on the night air. Dindie exchanged a long glance with her husband, elation flooding through her. Then he passed her the squalling, blood-covered scrap of humanity, so tiny and perfect that her fingers trembled to hold him as she wiped the red, indignant little face clear of mucus and swathed him warmly in Kit's saddle-sheepskin before laying him in his mother's arms.

"We'll name him for you, Major. It's the least we can do." Megs turned a radiant face to Kit, the agony of labour forgotten. "See, Arthur — ain't he lovely?"

Dindie scrambled to her feet, not wishing to intrude. Her muscles were cramped and she felt both exhilarated and drained. Heaven knows how Kit must feel.

He was scything a blanket in two, his face wearied and grimed with perspiration. She touched his arm.

"Will Megs be all right?"

"I hope so. I shall ask one of the doctors to attend her when we reach Bembibre." He glanced down at her, and said softly, "Your father would be proud of you, Dindie."

Her mouth trembled with emotion. "I only did as you instructed. What — what happens now?"

"Oh, we're not through yet. This next stage promises to take some time. Are you quite certain you feel up to assisting me?"

Dindie nodded dumbly. The weariness was closing in again but she fought it off. Together they returned to Megs.

It was late that night before they reached Bembibre, an ugly little town already rocking in fear from marauding bands of redcoats pursuing their fevered quest for liquor. Dindie's weariness was complete. When Kit returned from seeing Mrs Baillie safely into the hands of a medical officer he found her fast asleep, still slumped in the saddle.

She awoke next morning wrapped in Kit's army blanket. Realisation dawned that he must have taken her to headquarters for the night. There was an excruciating stiffness in her limbs but this was so constant an affliction now that she was able to shut her mind to the discomfort.

Her eyes rested involuntarily on the empty space which he had occupied, the blanket thrown aside as if in a great hurry. A confused tug of emotions fought within her, emotions which she had believed dead. And in face of all reason, a raw yearning that gnawed deep inside, and which caused her to colour hotly when she recognised in what circumstances it had its roots.

Reaching for the valise containing her personal belongings Dindie extracted her reticule and undid the strings, intending to unburden herself to the pages of her diary. It was her private solace, every entry a record of her heart laid bare. But as she

169

reached for the leather-bound volume her eye caught another object, bright and golden, half-hidden in the depths. Dindie held the wedding-ring in her palm, closing her eyes tightly against its accusing glow.

No, her head insisted! Where is your pride? Stand by your resolution . . .

Quickly she dropped the ring back into its muslin prison and snapped shut the valise. A sob pressed upwards in her throat and she felt a chilling loneliness encompass her.

*　　　*　　　*

It soon became apparent that the horrors committed in town the previous night exceeded those at Astorga. Over a thousand men belonging to the vanguard divisions had been found hopelessly incapacitated by drink, and as the Army moved out on the second day of January soldiers of the Reserve could be seen vainly trying to force on the barely conscious stragglers by kicks and prods with their bayonets. Many of the stupefied culprits were women and even children. They lay in the streets, wine trickling from their nostrils and lips like blood. One private was found drowned in a wine vat.

The 95th Rifles spent most of the day slapping faces into semi-consciousness, dragging or booting on as many as were capable of following in the wake of the departing Army but as night fell they were forced to leave, picking a path with Paget's cavalry through the mounds of insensible bodies which by next day would be helpless targets for the French as they trotted through the dirt-churned snow to rape and mutilate.

*　　　*　　　*

"I — I cannot go on, Kit! Leave me be, I beg you." Dindie subsided weeping into the snow. Driving rain slashed into her face and she had lost a shoe. She knew that she must rest, or die. They had pushed on six miles on foot, floundering in icy slush which stung her hacked legs and weighted her saturated skirts. Her pony

170

had had to be left behind some distance back and Kit had given up
his own horse to Megs Baillie.

"Please, Kit . . . I must sleep. I m-must!"

"You will go on, Dindie, because you can!" Roughly Kit jerked
her to her feet. "It's vital to keep your blood circulating freely.
Look," he relented, supporting her sobbing figure against him.
"We shall stop five minutes — no more!"

She sank thankfully to the ground and watched as he set about
hacking grimly at his leather boots with a knife.

"Wear these and don't argue," he commanded, forcing one of
her feet into the battered Hessian.

"Kit, your legs! . . ." Horrified, Dindie stared at his swollen,
angry flesh. Blood was trickling from a cut where he had unwittingly sliced the knife through.

Kit glanced down at the wound in mild surprise.

"Never felt the knife slip." He knelt before her unfastening her
sodden shoe and rubbed briskly at her foot.

"I cannot take your boots, Kit," protested Dindie.

"The devil — you shall!" He stood over her until she had pulled
them on. "Now get to your feet! We must catch up the column
before darkness falls. Put your arm about my waist like so — now,
do you remember how as children we used to recite Cowper on long
walks when your legs became tired?"

Her mouth trembled in a smile. " 'John Gilpin'?"

"That's the fellow." His arm encircled her body with a steely
strength. "How do the words go again?

> John Gilpin was a citizen
> Of credit and renown,
> A train band captain eke was he
> Of famous London town."

Dindie laughed weakly, concentrating fiercely upon forcing one
foot in front of the other. Kit was half-dragging her, for her own
strength was gone and she desired nothing so much as to sleep, to

lie down in that beckoning snow and never stir. But the driving
sleet willed her awake and he kept talking, or rather shouting at
her, making her answer, forcing her to use her legs.

> "The dogs did bark, the children screamed,
> Up flew the windows all;
> And every soul cried out, 'Well done!'
> As loud as he could bawl."

They continued in this fashion for over a mile, Kit bullying,
cajoling her into remaining awake whilst she struggled on in his
oversize boots, seeing through her tears and fogging weariness how
his own bare feet were blue and bleeding.

"Why will you not let me die, Kit?" she sobbed, after collapsing
for the twentieth time. "You could save yourself!"

"One of these days I shall tell you why," he returned, grimly. He
examined her face then without a word lifted her over his shoulder
and ploughed on set-faced in the wake of the slow-moving column.

Darkness was already fallen when just outside the village of
Cubilos they fell in with pickets belonging to Kit's regiment.
Dindie was immediately swathed in a blanket and someone produced brandy which Kit coaxed down her throat. As she clung
dazedly to him, feeling her insides heave as the raw liquor hit her
empty stomach, she glimpsed Jamie regarding her earnestly a few
yards away. He hesitated, as if deliberating whether or not to
approach, and when Dindie looked again he was gone.

She would have liked to call him back but the opportunity was
gone and she was cold and very, very tired. She lay back against
Kit's shoulder, fighting to stay awake. The night was bitterly cold,
the sky a mantle of black velvet chased by moonlight. It was a
gruesome experience, thought Dindie, shivering over a canteen of
skilly, to be huddled round a bivouac fire of branches with the
French behind and wolves howling all around. Several hussars
had been attacked earlier as they foraged in the icy wastes. Then
she remembered how nearly she had come to not reaching the

camp-fire at all, and closed her eyes tightly against the emotions at odds within her.

"I've eaten bullock and stewed mule but hang me if I can stomach maggots!" Kit tossed aside a ration biscuit with a shudder of distaste.

"Oh, I don't know," yawned a Guards officer who had joined their group. "They *are* cold to the palate but they do have a certain plump wholesomeness. Rather like oysters, I should imagine." He broke off, aghast. "My God — what's that?"

Some men of the 18th Hussars were conducting to the fire what appeared, to Dindie's eyes, to be a wild hog. The creature shambled on all fours with a sort of loping gait. It was not until the patrol sergeant stood in front of Kit with a breathless urgency that she saw The Thing was a man.

He was obviously one of the stragglers who had been overtaken and sabred by the French. He had drawn his shirt up to his face to shield his terrible wounds from the frosty air and when the sergeant removed this garment a concerted gasp of horror broke from the onlookers.

Not a single feature remained distinguishable. His ears had been cut off, his nose was slit and the flesh of his cheeks and lips hung in collops. What had once been a face was now raw, mangled pulp.

A scream rose in Dindie's throat. The creature was making pathetic whimpering noises as if trying to speak. Besides his terrible facial injuries he had been sabred in many other parts of his body.

"Bring him near the fire, for God's sake! And warm some wine." Very gently Kit lowered the man to a sitting posture. "It's incredible he should manage to survive at all! Where did you find him, Sergeant?"

"Creeping 'mongst some copsewood he was, sir. Couldn't hardly believe me eyes." The sergeant hesitated, regarding the blood-soaked head before them in horrified fascination. "Major . . . I think it's Flannigan."

173

Kit froze, staring hard at the macabre creature who was cowering close to the fire. Frostbite had evidently deadened all feeling in his limbs for he was raking the glowing embers towards himself with bare fingers in a manner horrible to behold.

Scooping a mugful of warmed wine Kit held it to the Irishman's lips, coaxing the liquid by degrees over his throat. Poor wretched sod. To come to this! Never in all the world would Kit have wished this fate on any man, not even Dan Flannigan.

"Shall we try him with some food?" muttered Cornet James Conolly. Kit shook his head.

"He will never be able to swallow." Laying a hand gently on the shaking, pain-contorted body, he asked, "Flannigan, can you understand me?"

The Thing uttered a groan and the shoulders heaved as though racked by silent sobs.

"We must send you on to the hospital at Villafranca. They will be better able to care for you properly."

Lord help me for that lie, thought Kit grimly. If Flannigan survived the next few hours it would be a miracle.

He delivered the private into the hands of Surgeon Underwood and went in search of Dindie, who was no longer before the camp-fire. Jamie glanced up with a reserved nod.

"She's by the dyke — being sick, I imagine."

"Thanks." They stared at each other in silence.

Dindie looked up ashen-faced, making no resistance as Kit touched her arm.

"He will die, won't he?" Her voice was a whisper.

"Don't waste any tears on Flannigan, Dindie!"

The rebuke slipped out harshly, without thought. The sight of her pinched with grief on account of the very cur whose hand had lit the powder-keg leading to their estrangement suddenly filled Kit with anger and resentment.

"How dare you say that? No matter how great a rogue, he is deserving of your compassion now!"

Her eyes, bright and accusing, held Kit's glance with a

something in their expression which caught his breath. With a stab of shock Kit discovered that his wife was grown into a woman.

"I believe you are secretly glad the French got Flannigan. Do you feel avenged, Kit? Is that it?"

"You are overwrought," he returned, coldly. "For the Lord's sake spare me your histrionics — I've had my bellyful of them, Dindie."

Her face blanched. "You shall suffer my inadequacies no further," she whispered, fighting to control her lower lip.

"Just what do you mean by that?"

Dindie sat down heavily on the low dry-stone wall.

"I — I'm leaving you, Kit. I mean to join the Vigo column at Lugo."

She saw his colour change. "Leave me? . . . You mean — for good?"

"I cannot make you happy. I am plain and stupid and a — a failure as a wife . . . You ought never to have married me, Kit. It was a mistake." She made a helpless little gesture of defeat.

"I have been mistaken in a great many things, it seems."

His eyes burned into hers with an intensity that made Dindie tremble. "Are you leaving me for Drummond?" he asked quietly.

"Would you care if I did?" she responded, wearily. "You seem to think I am able to exist without affection — that I need be nothing more than a mistress to you. But I want to be loved, Kit! Jamie understands that. He wishes to care for me and — and he will treat me kindly, I know," she added, with a fierce little smile.

"The devil he shall! You belong to me!" Kit gripped her shoulders with startling suddenness. "And you are sadly out, my girl! The southern column diverged soon after Astorga to protect our flank. It is already advanced miles along the Vigo road."

"But it cannot be! They said . . . "

Her eyes closed in bitter despair. It was just like her to have misheard. She ought to have realised that safety and the economics of their food situation must demand a separate route long before

Lugo. Through her dismay she saw Kit regarding her with an unspoken power of expression which she believed was possessed by no other eyes but his.

"I suppose it's no use my saying that I do love you," he said quietly.

She gazed at him without expression.

"What is love?"

"I'll tell you." He gripped her hands urgently. "It's wanting one special someone to strive for, share one's life and to have children by. It's . . . seeking that someone's happiness to the exclusion of self, laughing together, sharing . . . " He swallowed hard. "Don't you want all those things, Dindie?"

"I did — once."

At the tightness in her voice his expression altered, and he whispered, "Are you so unhappy with me, wifeling?"

Dindie could not bring herself to reply. Out of the corner of her eye she saw his face harden.

"If you are eating your heart out like a caged bird you shall have your freedom. Then you may marry Drummond or the Deuce — I dare say either will be preferable to you after me!"

Dindie watched him stride angrily back to the camp-fire. Tears pricked her eyes and there was a queer, empty feeling deep inside her that would not go away.

*   *   *

The following afternoon Kit took advantage of the commander-in-chief's preoccupation at their Villafranca headquarters to ride out with Colborne and Lord Paget to the advanced pickets posted farther down the hill just outside the sleepy village of Cacabelos. A hard frost overnight had crisped the ground to a treacherous slither, and so intent was Kit on his own tormented thoughts that more than once his horse stumbled and almost fell.

The picket screen provided by the green-jacketed riflemen and an arm of cavalry was positioned in a vineyard near a little stone bridge where the narrow stream crossed the road. The men were

176

grey with fatigue, having been harried constantly since Astorga by Soult's advance guard. Kit knew that the cavalry horses had not been unsaddled in four days and that the men slept bridle in hand.

Without warning a body of French chasseurs bore down upon them forcing the hussars to wheel round and ride as hard as they could back to the bridge, scattering the riflemen who were guarding the approaches. Hard on their heels came the French cavalry, sabres glinting in the thin sunshine. Kit recognised their commander as being the dashing young General Colbert of Marshal Ney's corps.

Within seconds the narrow bridge was jammed with riflemen, some of whom were drunk and discharging their firearms in all directions. Hussars were roaring out a warning and attempting to gallop their foaming horses through the impasse.

"Go back! Get into the houses!" shouted Kit, struggling to grip the reins with his injured hand. He glanced swiftly round and saw that both sides were in hopeless confusion. George Napier and some other of his fellow aides were thundering over the bridge towards General Moore, who was reined on horseback farther up the hill surveying the chaos, with the 52nd Regiment drawn up in scarlet ranks behind him. Of Colborne there was no sign.

A French chasseur bore down, blocking Kit's path. He saw the heavy sword flash and tried feverishly to parry the blow, lunging with every ounce of his strength.

*   *   *

George Napier found his chief in a great irritation. The enemy had been much closer than anyone had supposed. They had been as near as possible taken. And to crown Moore's annoyance his military secretary and Major Fane, both of whom ought to have known better, had again given way to impulse in pursuit of a skirmish with enemy cavalry.

It was not the conduct expected of experienced staff officers. Moore's already stretched patience was at snapping point and he turned to administer a caustic greeting to John Colborne, who was come spurring up having only narrowly escaped capture.

"Oh, I'm glad I've got someone at least! Where's Fane?"

"We went with Lord Paget, sir — to see where the French were . . . " Colborne reddened under the stinging rebuke.

"The enemy," returned the commander-in-chief, drily, "appear to be everywhere! General Paget's ophthalmia is not so dire as to require your wet-nursing. You happen to be more valuable to me alive."

Colborne, who had been in as great a fright as ever in his life, accepted the backhanded compliment meekly.

"At least we are buying time, sir. If we continue to hold their attention our main divisions should be well clear of Villafranca by nightfall."

Moore nodded, his temper cooling though only slightly. He had lost a number of riflemen in prisoners and there looked to be a fair amount of casualties choking the bridge. Where Fane was God only knew, but he was assured of the rough end of the general's tongue when he chose to show up, by Heaven he was! Abruptly, Moore snapped out an order.

"A battery of Horse Artillery, I think, and the 52nd withdrawn to the far bank. If Colbert decides to reform we shall be in readiness!"

*   *   *

Kit wiped his sabre with shaking fingers. It had been the closest shave of his career. He could still feel his steel slice down, still hear the Frenchman's gurgled scream before the fellow fell victim to the pounding hooves bearing down from behind.

A barrage of gunfire thundered from the ridge, causing his horse to rear up in terror. Sweating to regain control Kit realised with horror that he was caught directly in the firing range of their own artillery. A second blinding flash shot the animal from under him. Red-hot pain screwed through his leg and he felt himself flung helplessly to the ground by the tremendous impact. Someone was

178

dragging him clear, pulling his arms almost from their sockets . . .

Through a red haze he found himself staring at the sky. Private Flower's stricken face bent over, obscuring the boiling clouds.

"Major — Oh, God, sir . . . is he got bad?"

"Kit." The rich West Country burr was replaced by Jamie's choked exclamation. Weakly, Kit tried to sit up.

" 'Course I'm not bloody dead. Got me in the stumps, that's all."

He put an involuntary hand to his calf and found his fingers black with blood. Disbelieving he glanced down. His left foot and half the leg had been shot away.

13

DINDIE STARED UNSEEINGLY at her hands. She was aware of their uncontrollable shaking but her ears were straining at the sounds coming from the closed door of the adjoining room.

They would not allow her to see him. He had been brought directly to the priest's house with the other wounded. Her blood turned cold of a sudden. Why the priest's house? Was he going to die . . .

She stifled her panic. Somehow she must keep control. But how was she to remain calm not knowing even how badly injured Kit was? A low moan escaped her.

"Don't 'ee worry, lass. He'll not feel the knife. Shock be the soundest pain-killer I knows."

The speaker was a rifleman, one of the score of wounded waiting their turn on the surgeon's table. A bloodied handkerchief was twisted round his head and his hands dripped red from deep sabre slashes. Mechanically Dindie offered him a sip of water from the jug she had been handing round.

"I want to see him . . . " Tears filled her eyes.

"Lass, lass. You can't do your man no good in there." The rifleman looked at her kindly. "Ataking his leg off, be they?"

Dindie swayed. It was not, could not be true . . . With a piercing cry she ran to the door, feeling a hand clutch ice-cold at her heart.

"No, Dindie." Jamie barred her path into the room. "This is no place for you, my dear."

"Let me past, confound you! I will be with him!"

The sickly stench of blood hit her nostrils. Frenziedly she stared past Jamie to the surgeon who was bending over his instrument case setting out the grizzly tools of his profession in readiness.

"Kit . . . "

He was seated in an upright position on a mattress laid over the table. He greeted her with exuberance but his words were slurred from the wine they had given him as a stimulant and his grey eyes were sparkling bright.

"H'llo, wifeling." He pulled at her hand. "Come see this. Shot my bloody foot away — damn careless, don' you think, Dindie?"

Dindie gripped hard at his hand, feeling her limbs buckle. Below his knee the fibular bone stuck through the skin like the arm of the letter Y; part of his stocking had been caught and drawn into the wound which was discharging steadily and the crushed and bloodied mess of bone and cartilage had been tied tightly near the base in an effort to staunch the terrible bleeding. Beyond this hasty tourniquet his flesh ended abruptly.

Numbing horror hit and reverberated as she tried to smile for him through her tears. He was swearing loudly over the loss of his foot but it was evident that he was still in the grip of shock, probably not fully aware of the gravity of his injuries.

"Mrs Fane, I don't think you ought to — "

"I am staying here!" Dindie's eyes flashed with a piercing resolve. "I shall not faint, I promise you."

The surgeon stared hard at her. "Very well."

She watched in silence as he set about slitting open Kit's blood-matted overalls. He called for brandy, methodically soaking a sponge and swabbing the skin directly above the horrifying lesions. Her Papa had firmly believed in wounds responding to cold water treatment. Dindie supposed brandy was a grander extension of the same principle. She tried not to feel revulsion at sight of the filthy frock-coat he wore, so stiffly encrusted with dried blood and matter from former operations that it looked capable of standing by itself.

"Tourniquet."

Jamie took the binder from her trembling fingers and helped screw it firmly in place. Kit was talking loudly, exhorting them by turns to pass the brandy and go to the devil, even breaking into a snatch of popular song. It was like some hideous dream. The surgeon called for his scalpel and Dindie handed him the instrument case blindly, willing her nerves to remain strong.

He worked swiftly, so nimbly, indeed that it was over before she realised. Kit rebelled at any suggestion of a handkerchief over his eyes and instead turned his gaze upon her face with steadfast unflinching. He made not a murmur as the knife drove through and outwards in a sweeping circular motion. Dindie watched transfixed as the surgeon pulled back the two flaps of skin and sawed firmly through the bone while blood spurted from the great arteries, soaking his coat and hands.

In as many minutes the smashed stump had dropped to the floor and he was taking up the arteries and other vessels with a tenaculum and bringing across the flaps of skin, trimming and stitching them into place to make a purse-shaped wound.

"Hardly more blood than would fill a small bucket," declared the surgeon with satisfaction, wiping his hands. He felt Kit's almost imperceptible pulse and checked his blood pressure then turned to Dindie who was warming strips of black court-plaster before the fire, hardly aware of what she was doing.

"Once the muscles become rigid he will be in great pain, with probable haemorrhaging. There can be no question of removing him."

"But we must! The French . . . "

Dindie stared at him distraught. The medical officer continued his bandaging with brisk precision.

"I shall not be held answerable for the consequences if you do, Mrs Fane. You will kill him — you do realise that?"

"The enemy will kill him if we do not!" she whispered. "Would you leave him to their merciless butchery?"

She bent over her husband's pale face. He was slipping into unconsciousness. Tenderly Dindie kissed his brow. Never, while

182

breath remained in her body would she write his death warrant by having Paget leave him behind with a mere slip of paper requesting kind treatment from the first French commander who entered the town, as had been done at Sahagun with poor Lieutenant Penrice.

"Who knows if John Penrice is still alive?" she demanded bitterly, reading his thoughts. "No one! Well, my husband shall not be left behind to be cut to ribbons. If he dies it — it will be by God's will — not Lord Paget's!"

Fiercely she turned to Jamie. "Will you help me save Kit?"

James Drummond looked into her pale, young face so burning with purpose that she looked almost beautiful. Nothing he might say would alter her determination.

"Kit was my friend before he became your husband," he replied, simply.

*   *   *

The sixty miles from Villafranca up the long hill of Nogales to Lugo proved by far the worst of the retreat. During that terrible night piercing wind screamed down from the forbidding heights. Men crawled on hands and knees, punched to the ground by the icy force. Scores of starving wretches slumped into the snow never to rise again, and above their dying groans the hills echoed with shots as another tough cavalryman knelt weeping beside his favourite horse.

Tom Jackson pushed grimly on in the line of bloodied footmarks. Dead and dying choked the roadside, half-buried under broken carts, spiked guns and the already frozen corpses of bathorses and children. There were not many women left now. Many had been left behind long before Villafranca too ill or drunk to force themselves on. Some might drag themselves painfully to a ditch or a mountain hut. Yet even there no safety could be guaranteed. A patrol of French dragoons had only the previous night dragged out three such stragglers and taken it in turns to rape them before leaving them in the snow to die. Jackson thanked God that he had had the sense to leave Mary at home in England.

He had rejoined the regiment at Villafranca. His back was virtually healed. Only the mental scar remained. They had told him about Flannigan, expecting him perhaps to feel a satisfaction. Jackson could summon no sense of retribution, only pity.

Yet even pity was a rare emotion now. He had watched in horror as a woman fell up to her waist in a sucking bog. As she slid helplessly down through the freezing slime the men trudging behind walked over her head. Every soldier viewed his neighbour as a means of furthering his own comfort. The instant a man fell down some other would have the boots from him or his knapsack ransacked for non-existent crumbs.

"Mr Jackson . . . is it really you?"

Mrs Fane parted the canvas of a plodding spring waggon in front. Jackson was shocked to see how thin she had become. He had heard about the major's foot from young Flower. It was a bad business losing a limb. Jackson owed Major Fane a great deal, and had always felt a protective interest in this slip of a girl whose undaunted courage must have been severely tested these last hours.

Resting a hand on the waggon's hooped framework he trudged alongside. At his enquiring after the major she shook her head wordlessly.

"He has a raging fever," she said at last, in a choked voice. "I have tried ice to reduce his temperature but I — I dread he may contract pneumonia if I continue."

"But you are keeping him warm?" persisted Jackson, quickly.

"Yes, oh yes! Only I do not know what else to try. Oh Papa," she whispered to herself, "if only you were here."

She slipped back to Kit's side, fearful of what she might find. He lay on the jolting waggon floor, his head pillowed on the coat taken from a dead soldier. Dindie wrung out a cloth in a bucket of melted snow and pressed it to his forehead. He was muttering beneath his breath in a low delirium and he remained violently flushed and restless.

The surgeon had given her a draught of Peruvian bark to

184

administer but she dared not try him with it for fear he might choke. She wiped the sweat from his body, trying to pray in incoherent gasps that made no sense. She was wearied beyond all feeling yet she dared not close her eyes. She knew by the violence of his fever that the wound must be infected. It was tumid, angry-looking and swollen and was begun to suppurate, which the surgeon said must be regarded as a healthy sign. Dindie did not believe him.

At each halt she checked the bloodied dressing with care. Sometimes Kit tried to sit up, grappling with her, swearing wrathfully to leave him be, his eyes fever-glazed and staring. If Jamie had not held him down she would never have managed to remove the slimy bandages, for the fever seemed to have given him a maniacal strength and she feared for his reason.

With trembling fingers Dindie smoothed the hair from her husband's damp brow. It was matted and crawling with lice like her own. Once such depths of degradation would have paralysed her with horror. Personal hygiene had always been second nature to her. Now vermin was merely one aspect more of the hell in which they found themselves Dindie had not felt soap and water touch her skin in over a sennight, she had lived in the same clothes for far longer — yet somehow it no longer mattered. In this charnel-house of north-west Spain only survival remained meaningful.

Over and over her tortured thoughts burned in a confused agony of self-reproach. If they had not parted on that note of bitter finality, if she had not confessed her decision to leave him might Kit's terrible fate have been averted? How badly had his concentration been affected? Dindie could only guess, and in the depths of her despair and remorse she would fling herself to the jolting waggon-floor, crying softly and beating her fists against the wooden spars until her knuckles ran with blood.

Tom Jackson plodded resolutely on behind the lumbering waggon as it inched through the slush. The wind was biting and in the darkness it was all too easy to miss one's footing. The road zig-zagged here through the heart of the wine-growing country, carried in places high above rushing torrents which only weeks ago had been picturesque streams. It was hard to imagine how in summer this same stretch of countryside must be enchanting, with the wooded ravines plunging in green-hued majesty to the valley floor. Seeing it now, silent and barren under a blanket of ice littered with dying men, Jackson acknowledged the awesome invincibility of Nature.

A crowd of soldiers attracted his attention. They were gathered in jostling silence round some object which he could not see and he joined them, knowing it must be no common occurrence that could evoke compassion in their blunted emotions.

By the flickering light of a torch he saw the stiffened corpse of a young woman. She lay half-covered in snow with a baby still sucking frantically at her frozen breast. The infant could be no more than a few days old. Jackson pushed forward and gathered up the child, wrapping it warmly inside his dolman. It was only when he glanced more closely at the corpse of its mother that he recognised the familiar features of Megs Baillie.

Stony-faced, Jackson motioned one of the gawping men to the sodden blanket with which the sergeant's wife had tried pathetically to stave off the icy hand of Death.

"Cover her up, damn you," he muttered. He glanced down at the tiny face poking from the half-fastened jacket.

"We had best find your Pa," he declared.

*   *   *

Gabriel Flower stared at the pistol in his hand. He couldn't do it. He just couldn't. Beside him in the snow Sally lay with her head lolling across his knees. Her hooves gushed blood for lack of shoeing and she was utterly done. Sobbing, Flower laid his head against the mare's soft muzzle. She was dying in agony and he could not summon the guts to pull the trigger.

He remained on his knees a long time, or so it seemed. Dull-eyed, he watched the pitiful procession of scarecrow-like figures

186

battling on the long hill. The snow was strewn for miles with soldiers spent with exhaustion or intoxication, frozen or near death. An officer of the guards shuffled painfully past him, with pieces of old blanket wrapped round his feet. As the ragged aristocrat limped out of sight Flower heard one private remark with malicious satisfaction,

"There goes three thousand a year!"

Lord Paget also passed close by, riding slowly. His horse was being led by a tall officer of the 28th Regiment who looked more like a mountain shepherd, wearing as he did an Army blanket with a hole cut for his head. Lord Paget's eyes were bound by a white handkerchief but his bearing remained handsomely erect.

"Flower! What the devil are you about? Do you want to freeze to death?" Tom Jackson shook roughly at his shoulder.

"I don't care no more. Sal's dying . . . reckon I'll as soon die with her." Flower broke down afresh, his fingers caressing the mare's straggling mane. "I knows I got to finish her off but — I *can't*, Mr Jackson!"

Jackson heard the choked despair in heartfelt silence. The fight had gone out of the lad. He lived only for the poor mangled beast beside him and Jackson knew Flower meant what he said about wanting to die with the animal.

Withdrawing the tiny squirming bundle from his dolman Jackson thrust the child into Flower's startled arms.

"I'm entrusting this life to your charge, lad," he said firmly. "And Lord help you if you don't deliver it safe to Arthur Baillie. It's all he has left now," he added softly. "Now on your feet sharpish! I'll see to your horse for you. She'll not feel a thing, I promise."

Bemusedly Flower complied. Jackson watched him stumble back to the road clutching the infant, then slowly he got out his pistol.

*　　*　　*

The Roman walls of Lugo were reached on January 5th. The

magazines there contained both food and ammunition but this alone was not the attraction which now brought considerable numbers of stragglers sidling back to rejoin their regiments. The commander-in-chief had decided to make a stand.

This expectation of battle was, however, more welcome to his troops than to Moore himself. He had made his decision only with reluctance. He despaired of engaging the French with an Army which had so consistently let him down by their gross misconduct, an Army which had totally changed in character since the retreat began.

But it was not only the troops which caused him frustration. He had sent George Napier galloping furiously with orders to General Baird to make for Corunna with the leading divisions, instead of Vigo as originally planned. But Baird, still in bed and in a foul temper at being woken so early, sarcastically informed Napier that he would send one of his own dragoons to relay the orders to the other commanders. But the courier got drunk and by the time word was received to turn back four hundred men had already died on the terrible road to Vigo.

Moore was also deeply saddened by the loss of his chief 'galloper'. He had arranged that Major Fane was to be quartered under his own roof at Lugo, where every attention was to hand and where young Mrs Fane might be relieved of her lonely vigil. But with a tigerish vehemence that surprised everyone Mrs Fane had dared them to move her husband whilst his fever still raged, and not even the general's intervention could shake her determination. He had reasoned firmly with her, noting with compassion how fiercely her eyes burned as she shielded his aide's fever-wracked body from all comers.

"If you move him he may haemorrhage! I can perfectly manage — truly." She turned her tear-streaked face to Moore's, whispering tremulously, "I thank you, sir, for your generous offer, but God will give me the strength to carry on."

Against that impassioned conviction there was little the general could do but ensure that she ate the food he ordered to be sent out to her, and arrange for the major to have the best medical attention available.

Though still deeply vexed by Baird's blunder he put it behind him and concentrated his energies on troop morale. From his earliest days as an ensign Moore had learned the value of restoring self-respect to disheartened, weary men. He gave orders for the distribution of pipeclay and watched with satisfaction the mood of optimism near to cheerfulness which swept through the Army. In their sparkling white cross-belts and polished buttons the gaunt, ragged military held their heads higher. They began to look and feel like soldiers once more.

His staff, however, witnessed that other side so different from the sustained confidence that lent inspiration to the men. It was his aides who saw him slump in the privacy of his quarters at the day's end, his face worn down with despair and disappointment. More than once George Napier had glimpsed a suspicion of tears in the chief's eyes. The appalling outrages committed by the infantry, the agonising business of the retreat itself had pierced his heart. Napier's dark eyes burned. He would have given anything he possessed to restore a smile to that careworn countenance.

Even the resurgence of spirits at the prospect of battle failed to persuade Sir John that the tide might be turning. When Colonel Graham attempted to draw him on the subject he received scant encouragement.

"After we've beaten them you will take us on in pursuit of them a few days, won't you?"

Moore dipped his brush in a mug of hot water and steadfastly continued shaving. His generals travelled with opulent toilet sets containing the finest monogrammed steel. Their commander-in-chief contented himself with a plain full-size Palmer razor and strop, Army issue.

"No," he retorted. "I have had enough of Galicia."

"Oh!" Graham had expected a more favourable response. "But just a few days after them — you must take us," he argued.

Moore carried on shaving without making reply.

That same day brought also an unsparing General Order. As usual its wording angered many officers who felt with some justification that no exertion on their parts could have stemmed the floodgates of violence and drunkenness.

" 'The Commander of the Forces is tired of giving orders which are never attended to . . . He was forced to order one soldier shot at Villafranca and he will order all others to be executed who are guilty of similar enormities.' My God, he don't half mean business!"

"If he had let us fight at the outset we'd not have been plagued with a tenth of these excesses! Lord knows we might have subsisted for weeks if he had set himself to defend the passes."

James Drummond turned away disgusted by the grumbling. Whatever they might argue the Order was not unjust. The cavalry had not broken nor the Reserve and Guards regiments, simply because they exerted a higher standard of discipline. A regiment was only as strong as its weakest link.

He sought out Dindie and found her keeping vigil over her husband's fevered ramblings. She had not slept for two nights and she looked close to collapse. She welcomed him with a weary smile, pushing back the lank hair from her face. But behind the smile her mouth was trembling and he knew instinctively that Kit was worse.

"Thank God you are come." She watched dull-eyed as Jamie knelt by her husband's side. During the long hours of waiting her spirits had wavered between hope and despair. Kit was still dangerously flushed and her arms ached from wiping away the pools of perspiration that glistened afresh almost as soon as she was done. But during the last hour Kit's body had turned frighteningly cold. In despair Dindie had lain down next him in his rough bed and clasped him in her arms, praying that the heat from her own body might generate the warmth he so vitally needed. She was terrified of exerting undue pressure for fear of bleeding yet she knew with dread certainty that if she failed to maintain his body heat Kit must die.

When Jamie tiptoed quietly to her side she was weeping softly into Kit's shoulder, her body covering his protectively and her face white with strain. Jamie begged her to let him take over the vigil but she shook her head fiercely.

"I shall not leave him," she whispered. "Not now — not ever!"

Jamie sat himself on the rough waggon floor, prepared to wait with her till Domesday, if need be. She remonstrated, reminding him of the impending stand against the French and the necessity of his securing a night's sleep. In the faint glow from the waggon-lantern she looked small and defenceless crouched by Kit's side with his head in her lap. Jamie ached to take her in his arms. Theirs was a curious relationship, he brooded. He knew his own feelings only too well, but as for hers . . . Instinctively his hand reached out to stroke her hair.

"I meant what I said, Dindie — about wanting to care for you if — if anything should happen to Kit," he said softly.

"I know," she whispered huskily. "I do know it."

"I quite realise you don't care for me as you do Kit but — oh, Dindie, might you not come to feel something towards me?"

"I do care, Jamie . . . you are my dearest friend and I love you," she returned choked with emotion. "But you deserve more than second-best, and I know if Kit were to — to die I should not want to go on living."

"My dear, I just want you to know, that's all."

He remained talking quietly with her, describing his parents, his home in Scotland, anything that might take her mind from the chill shadow of death that hovered by Kit's bed and she listened not speaking, holding her husband close, willing him to live by the sheer depth of her love.

Soon after, a rapid change ensued. Kit's skin became dry and alarmingly hot. With dismay Dindie found his pulse was rapid as it had been in the first flush of fever after the amputation. Whilst Jamie hurried to fetch a surgeon she piled Kit's burning body with all the blankets and coats that could be got, knowing that only by inducing heavy sweating could they hope to break his fever. Then she fell on her knees and prayed as she had never prayed before, great salt tears slipping wetly through her fingers.

She must have dozed for upon opening her eyes she found herself lying by his side and saturated with wet. Her first terrified thought was that Kit was bleeding to death and her hands shook so badly as she stumbled to bring the lantern close that she dropped it.

But it was not blood. Kit lay quiet, streaming with heavy perspiration. Dindie slumped over him mingling her tears with his sweat. Dimly she knew that she ought to pray, to thank God for this miracle but she could do nothing but press her face close to Kit's breast and sob.

14

EARLY THE NEXT morning Marshal Soult began to feel out the British position. To his dismay, instead of finding himself up against Paget's heroic rearguard as he had supposed, fifteen guns blazed back from the opposing height and the French battery was immediately put out of action. It was clear that he had not only the Reserve but the whole of Moore's Army in front of him.

Sir John himself had been out at daybreak to inspect the whole of the British line and throughout the morning his aides were employed non-stop, unable even to snatch time to appease their hunger. Major Charles Napier, the able young commander of the 50th Regiment, was enjoying a hearty breakfast with his friend Charles Stanhope, when they espied his brother George come galloping along their part of the line. The two immediately ran up to greet him, thrusting their steaming canteens under his nose in wicked satisfaction.

"You dainty dog! You can't eat Irish stew!"

George Napier, who had eaten nothing since the night before, swore good-naturedly at this brotherly taunt.

"Damn you both for your exquisite lack of feeling!" he shouted, setting spurs to his charger. "You will be well served if Soult decides to take your breakfast from you!"

From the heavy barrage which drowned his last words it appeared a strong probability. Undismayed by the British strength the enemy were pushing hard. But Moore was ready, his troops, though numbering no more than eighteen thousand, were now revived and exhibiting superb confidence, and when he rode into their midst waving his cocked hat to encourage and rally them they pressed forward cheering. Upon his command they emptied their muskets into the French and then hurtled down upon the advancing enemy infantry, stabbing with their bayonets like men possessed.

By evening Soult's men had pulled back and now began a desperate war of nerves. All next day Moore waited anxiously from across the gently sloping valley willing his opponent to attack. He feared Soult meant to wait for reinforcements to come up and outflank him.

And as the precious hours ticked away Moore knew that if the attack did not come he must be forced to quit the field and continue their retreat. There was not enough food left to wait another day.

At nine o'clock that night the order to retire was given. Bivouac fires were left burning to deceive the enemy and pickets remained behind to tend the flames. Only by creeping away under cover of darkness could the British hope to gain a few hours start on their pursuers.

Above the rising wind and rapping of torn canvas from the broken-down spring waggon, Dindie slumped wearily beside her sleeping husband, listening to the outbreak of grumbling as the troops took to the road. Always it was the same. Why were they not being allowed to chase after the Duke of Damnation and his miserable Army? Had they not already proved beyond doubt that although starving, frost-bitten, filthy and in rags this British force had the guts to trounce Bonaparte's mounseers?

The curses were swiftly borne away in a vicious howling gale that slashed rain into Dindie's face as she clung to the hooped framework, gasping with cold and alarm. A gaping hole had been rent in the canvas and she tried to prevent the piercing cold from reaching Kit by stuffing bits of blanket into the torn bodywork but they were blown away almost immediately. Through the hole she could see how the trusses of straw placed en route to mark the line of march were hopelessly scattered. Soldiers were stumbling into ditches, unable to pull themselves out through sheer exhaustion. One man was already said to have drowned.

The hurricane had blown out the lantern flame and through the blackness she could hear Sadie O'Flynn's little boys at the front end of the waggon screaming in terror as a tremendous crack shuddered through the vehicle, lurching it to a sudden halt. Dindie was flung to the hard floor by the impact and her forehead struck some hard object in the darkness, rendering her momentarily stunned.

Through her dazed senses she heard Tom Jackson's voice shouting at her to get up, then strong hands were pulling her to safety and in the same instant the waggon framework collapsed in a grinding crash of timber.

"The children! Oh, someone pull them out quickly!" A cold hand clutched at her heart. "Kit," she whispered. "Oh, God — Kit is still in there!"

Hardly able to see, she crouched against the screaming gale wordless at what they might find.

"It's all right, Dindie." Jamie's voice close by penetrated her numbed brain. "Kit is unharmed — so far as I can judge. We've laid him over here." His arm gripped hers firmly. "Don't give way to despair. We shall lash some of these timbers together to fashion a stretcher. Jackson!" His voice rose against the wind's fury. "Find me a length of rope, forage-cords, anything will suffice!"

During that tempestuous night whole brigades lost their bearings on the dark mountainside. Guides wandered aimlessly leading columns down winding lanes and over stone walls only to end up hopelessly lost, and as rain continued to pour down the disconsolate troops sank into the mud, tortured by hunger.

The first light of dawn creeping over the horizon saw the British Army begin to drop down towards the coast. After an appalling slog of two hundred and fifty miles with the French hard on their heels the harsh mountains of Galicia were finally behind them. They had emerged from their Dark Valley into what seemed like a different world. Here in the fertile farmland of the plain the wind was soft. Orange and lemon trees waved blossoming branches in welcome and beyond the intersecting stone walls field upon field of rye was in ear. Men hobbling along with rags bound round their bleeding feet paused in momentary respite from their agony to stare in disbelief.

For Gabriel Flower the descent to Betanzos was reminiscent of Bunyan's description of Christian beholding the Celestial City. Only it was not faith alone that lifted the dragging feet of his comrades but the promise of food. Beyond Betanzos the road dipped in a series of twelve twisting miles to the sea. Once over the next hill Corunna would lie before them, its bay crowded with the waiting transports fluttering the flags of the Royal Navy.

General Moore had ridden ahead to the bridge at Burgo just outside Corunna to witness his Army march across and into the town. Patches of ice still glistened on the road but the sun was trying to break through and the hedgerows were bright with wild iris and valerian. Moore's spirits soared. Spring was already on its way promising a re-birth, a renewal of hope.

As each regiment marched past its commander-in-chief soldiers straightened aching backs and stepped out smartly. Every commanding officer rode in front and captains and subalterns flanked their sections with due precision. General Moore spoke a few words to each regiment as it approached the bridge, complimenting and castigating as he thought fit.

Harry Percy, reined in behind the chief, murmured gleefully to Napier that the general was in high gig again. Gone was the melancholic hauteur, the despair. Astride his charger taking the salute Moore's fine features looked almost boyish.

By three in the afternoon the last brigades came up and one in particular arrested Sir John's admiration. Drums tapping the soldiers marched in column of sections with the drum-major twirling his staff and displaying all the panache associated with a Hyde Park review. Sheer professionalism of step and bearing showed proudly through the ragged, bleeding ranks.

"These," commented Moore to his staff with acute satisfaction, "must be the Guards."

*   *   *

An explosion of startling intensity rocked Corunna, bringing women and children rushing screaming into the bustling streets. Dindie crossed the courtyard leading to the headquarters-house, picking a path through fallen masonry and glass and trying not to spill the bowl of steaming broth in her hands. Kit must have it at all costs.

She had left him sleeping easily upstairs. His breathing was regular now although he frequently cried out in pain. Not for the world would she disturb him, only her heart knew a quickening of fear each time she gazed on his hollow, wasted face. So light had he become that Jamie and Tom Jackson had carried him between them with little effort on the final stretch from Lugo. Jackson's burning devotion drew her overwhelming gratitude but when she had tried to express her feelings he smiled shyly and shook his head.

"The major has been good to me and the missus." He hesitated. "I'd like fine if he'd let me stay with him once we get back home, Mrs Fane. He'll require a strong fellow to do for him."

Voices reached Dindie as she entered the house. Moore's headquarters were situated on the fashionable Canton Grande, a sweep of gracious but decaying residences overlooking the harbour. She found Jamie on the stairs remonstrating with a half dozen chambermaids and female servants who were in a frenzy of hysteria fearing the explosion was a sign that the French were come up. He sent them packing with a broadside of ripe Spanish and greeted Dindie with an embarrassed grin.

"Don't be alarmed. The engineers have succeeded in blowing up the bridge at Burgo, we think." Taking her arm he said gently, "Dindie . . . Kit is awake."

She exclaimed and made to break into a run but he held her back. "Take it canny, won't you? He is very weak."

197

"What does he say?" she whispered, aware that she was trembling for no reason. Jamie gave her a queer little smile.

"Nothing much. I did most of our talking. Go in to him — and mind he finishes that broth."

Dindie hung up her tattered cloak with deliberate care before turning towards the bed. How thankful she was that General Moore had given instruction that Kit should not be disturbed. Percy and George Napier were her dear friends but to have a roomful of aides looking on when she wanted to be alone with Kit would be intolerable. Yet her heart fluttered unaccountably and she felt all at once shy of him.

He was watching her intently, following her every move. Dindie bent over, laying one hand lightly upon his.

"Hello, Kit."

He gazed up at her accusingly. "Where have you been? Jamie says you went to the kitchen ages ago." There was a heat in his voice despite its weakness. Dindie helped him to a sitting position and coaxed a spoonful of broth to his lips.

"Please try some, Kit — you must rebuild your strength."

"I am not altogether inept," he spluttered, swallowing it down protesting. He sank back against the pillow spent with the effort, and turned his face towards her.

"I understand I have you to thank for saving my life."

Dindie looked away, her eyes filling with sudden tears at this unbearable formality. "I — I could scarce let you die." Her voice choked on the words. She could feel his glance burning her cheeks. Against the white pillow his skin was flushed.

"Jamie tells me you are in love with me. Is that true, Dindie?"

His directness so overpowered her that she was unable to answer. She could only raise his hand to her cheek and hold it there. A smile parted his cracked lips and he tried to whisper her name but he could manage no more than a croak.

"Oh, Kit . . . my own darling."

Awkwardly his fingers drew her face close and they kissed. It was neither as long nor as practised as Kit was capable of but to

198

Dindie his clumsy spontaneity raced her heart as no other kiss could have done.

They drew apart and she slipped to her knees, resting her cheek next to his on the pillow. Their fingers entwined with a gentle pressure.

"I love you, wifeling." His voice was muffled, almost inaudible and his grey eyes held hers in a long, long glance.

"I know it," returned Dindie softly, "now."

His eyelids closed contentedly and he fell silent, exhaustion taking over afresh. Dindie stroked his brow, content to let matters rest. Later there would be time for healing the wounds, for saying all the things that lovers say.

"My left leg throbs like blazes, Dindie," he fretted. "Did I take a pounding? My head feels so muzzy . . . "

A lump of tears pressed upwards in her throat. He had turned away from her, his face half-buried in the pillow. Then his eyelids fluttered and she saw his mouth quiver wryly.

"Confoundedly rich, that. I remember now — they cut it off. They cut my bloody leg off . . . "

His face buried suddenly into her breast and a strangled sob escaped him. Flinging her arms about him Dindie held her husband close, comforting, whispering fierce encouragement whilst her tears splashed unchecked down his chest.

"What sort of future can I offer you now? A half-pay major with a cork leg . . . I have no right to expect it of you."

At the bitterness in his tone Dindie's eyes flashed.

"So you consider yourself a cripple, do you?" she raged. "Do you dare to presume I think you any less a man because of that? If you must know, Kit Fane, I'm glad you are out of the fighting! Have you any notion how it feels to wait in anguish, dreading each knock at the door lest it bring word of you dead or — or . . . "

Sobbing, she pressed her face into his chest. Kit's arms tightened about her and she felt his fingers caress the nape of her neck.

"My poor, brave love," he murmured, unsteadily. "Then you really do care, despite the unpardonable act which I — " His voice

199

failed, and he closed his eyes tight for an instant, continuing in a bare whisper, "I never intended to hurt you, little bird. I swear!"

"It belongs to the past." Dindie laid a forefinger lightly against his lips. "I thought — after it happened — that my heart had forgotten how to love you, that I could never forgive. I almost succeeded in convincing myself."

He reached down and kissed her fiercely. For a long moment they clung together. Dindie's heart beat hard, and her body trembled with a burning awakening under his touch.

"I had no conception that my little wife was so warm-blooded," murmured Kit, smiling at her tiredly. They exchanged an intimate, lingering glance, then Kit's expression altered and he lay back, drawing her head down against his shoulder with a little groan.

"Oh, Dindie — I want nothing so much as to share the rest of my life with you. I'm tired of playing the field — life is too short and precious. I've seen too many fine men die without cause these past weeks not to realise it . . . though after you confessed how you wanted to leave me I did not much care if I lived or died. It was only when I read this —" his hand reached out and thumbed through the diary which she had unwittingly left within reach — "that I realised there might still be a chance for me."

"You — have read my journal?" Scarlet-cheeked, Dindie dared to meet his eyes. He was smiling penitently, yet with an amused tenderness which beggared any attempt at remonstrance.

"It was abominably wrong, I own, but I do not repent of it. How else would I have discovered how passionately your emotions run concerning me?" He looked directly into her eyes with a something in his glance that sent desire, sharp as a knife, searing through her. "Are you perfectly resolved to share my old age — or am I to petition Parliament for a divorce?"

She made a sound somewhere between a laugh and a sob.

"Only if you wish it."

"Do you honestly believe I should be mooncalfed enough to release you, precious girl?" He sighed deeply. "I've given you the devil of a time, Dindie. If I had not become involved with Paquita you would have been spared the horror and anguish of the whole sordid business."

Dindie swallowed hard. "When she died I — I was persuaded you must hate me for ever, Kit."

He crushed her against him with a fierceness that banished any such notion. "If any blame attaches to Paquita's death it must be mine alone."

At the whispered self-recrimination Dindie uttered a little cry and wound her arms softly about his neck. They kissed and could not stop kissing. Then the recollection of the cooling broth caused Dindie to detach herself with a supreme effort from her husband's arms, saying shakily, "And to think I supposed your energies gone." She rubbed at her face, protesting with a laugh, "Your beard tickles."

"I feel like a savage," admitted Kit, ruefully feeling the growth on his chin. "And I itch prodigiously. Am I lousy?"

"Yes," retorted Dindie, holding out the spoon. "So am I. So is everyone — and please to open your mouth wide, sir."

A lurking gleam fired his eyes and he strove to catch at her waist but collapsed, gasping in agony. Dindie hung over him, her face blanched. When the spasm had subsided Kit forced a smile, saying weakly, "Insult my palate with that foul skilly if you must — but you had best procure a measure of opium besides from Surgeon Underwood, lovey. My stump is aching rather."

*   *   *

Soon after daylight next day Sir John Moore left his headquarters on the Canton Grande and with a small party of staff officers rode out to reconnoitre the rolling country around Corunna. It now looked as though he must prepare to fight one battle more. His leading divisions had reached the coast eager for their first glimpse of the rescue fleet. But the Bay of Corunna lay empty.

Within the next twenty-four hours naval vessels did begin to arrive but they proved to be only hospital and store ships. Where were the transports which he had so urgently requested? Still beating, presumably, against fierce head winds — even in this final desperate lap the elements seemed bent on confounding his efforts.

If Admiral Hood arrived within the next two days the Army, pray God, would be evacuated by the skin of its teeth. If no ships came . . . Moore's heart sank at the possibility. He had lost six thousand men during this terrible retreat. Now perhaps his survivors, the verminous, dysentery-ridden, indomitable survivors of the only Army his country possessed were to be fatally trapped with their backs to the sea.

He watched the twin columns of dense black smoke billow slowly over the part of town where the ammunition magazines had been. Realising that the French must reach him before embarkation could be completed he had ordered the immediate destruction of all excess stores, including more than a thousand barrels of gunpowder which had not been used.

Snapping open his spy-glass Moore trained it between the twin hill ranges sloped in gorse and rough boulders to the little village of Elvina. Its brown pantiled roofs glistened with early frost. If he was correct in his assumptions this cluster of stone dwellings would be the vital hinge upon which rested either victory or the blackest day in British military history.

*   *   *

Jamie trudged slowly up the beach, his face mask-like. Behind and around him the strand was blood-splashed with the carcases of dead and dying horses, pathetic mounds of skin and bone. He had thought himself inured to death and suffering until now.

He tried to shut his mind to the grisly task. Through the acrid pistol-smoke he recognised tough cavalry veterans of his own company weeping unashamedly as they prepared to despatch their favourite horses. Jamie tried to convince himself that it was better the animals should be shot now than worked to death by the Spaniards or the French but the appalling clumsiness of the

202

operation turned his stomach. Above him on the cliffs overhanging the beach more horses were being dragged to the edge to be shot and pushed over. So distressed were many of the dragoons, however, that some poor brutes landed on the sands still alive because of a badly aimed shot, and had to be finished off with hammer blows or cut throats.

It was sickly work. Above the terrified neighing of the chargers and the pounding hooves of those which had broken free the air was alive with birds wheeling in raucous cry. Not only gulls and sandpipers — he recognised the dread black vultures drawn by the rotting carrion waiting to gorge themselves. Jamie prayed fervently that it might never be his lot to be wounded and left dying on a field of battle. He had seen too many companions with their eyes picked out by these chilling harbingers of Death.

"Cap'n, me sabre's buckled."

Jamie recognised the anguished sob in the young cavalryman's voice, knew there was nothing wrong with the weapon that a steady hand would not set to rights. Automatically, he drew his own sword and offered it but the private shook his head, wordless with grief. Jamie glanced down at the pathetic, pain-maddened stallion, so butchered through fear and inexperience that it was difficult to make out its convulsive twitching through the dark pool of blood.

Swiftly and cleanly he severed the horse's throat. Blood spurted everywhere, soaking his hands and uniform and in his ears the calm swish of the surf mocked incongruously as it broke foaming white on the sand. Closing his eyes tight, Jamie forced himself to finish the grisly assignment.

*   *   *

Dindie heard a clock chime eleven from somewhere in the darkened town. Rising softly she tiptoed to one of the glass-fronted balconies and stared out at the winking string of lights suspended from the double avenue of trees fronting the Canton Grande. In the harbour fishing smacks were putting out to sea. From the glass-enclosed *miradores* it was possible to discern the black outline of the

203

old town descending to the Pescaderia, or fish-market, with the towering ramparts of the citadel dominating all.

She heard Kit turn in his sleep. He was drugged to make bearable the pain. Her every footstep echoed mournfully in the still room, for all personal belongings were already packed up in readiness for departure. Orders had been given for the embarkation of the wounded, all dismounted cavalrymen and such stores as could be accommodated. As the terrain around Corunna was unsuitable for cavalry they would not be required in the coming battle. General Moore had assured her that Kit would be taken on board as soon as the first ships anchored in the bay.

Soon, thought Dindie exultantly, the long nightmare would be ended. A few days at sea and they would sight England and home. It occurred to her that Kit and she did not have a home of their own, at least not yet. Would Grandfather Hurst still refuse to acknowledge her, she wondered sadly? For her own part she would be content sharing the meanest cottage so long as she might be with Kit, but Linkdown was his inheritance and she knew that he could not be happy anywhere else.

Returning to his bedside she lay down next to him, but sleep refused to come. Her mind was too alert, too full of the morrow. It would be hard saying goodbye to all the many friends she had made during the last months, harder still to recall those with whom she had not been granted the privilege of a farewell . . . Cheerful, blunt-spoken Megs Baillie, whose tiny infant was thriving against all the odds whilst Megs herself lay cold beneath the snow somewhere on the terrible hill of Nogales; chirpy cavalry faces which had lightened the long march with their songs and good humour now only names. Tears pricked her eyes. In that instant she realised fully just how fortunate a deliverance was hers. Though bird-thin through worry and lack of food she had come through unscathed. The husband whom she loved above all else was disfigured for life, but they had each other, they had survived.

Impulsively, Dindie rose and slipped on her cloak, then with a glance of reassurance at her sleeping husband she hastened from the room. There was one other of whom she must take leave and she was resolved to do it now, whilst her courage ran high.

Sir John Moore shook the sleep from his bloodshot eyes and scrawled a final paragraph to the long letter he had been composing. It was directed to the Secretary for War and bore ample witness to the general's exhaustion. Written in a barely decipherable scrawl the despatch was ink-spattered and mis-spelt, with words crossed out and frequently missed. But he was too tired to care. Reports were coming in thick and fast that the French were come up and positioned on the longer of the two hill ranges overlooking the town. For his own satisfaction he must furnish Castlereagh with an understanding of the dilemma which had prompted the decision to retreat and he had done so, unburdening his heart, neglecting nothing of the ugly, painful saga.

He was so preoccupied that at first he was unaware of the little figure who entered softly. In the shadows thrown by the branch of candles on his desk her appearance suggested the ghost of a memory which refused to die—the remembrance of a fresh-faced brunette waving goodbye with the warm Sicilian breeze tossing her bonnet-strings and a little terrier dog in her arms.

"Caroline? . . . "

Dindie's eyes misted at the hoarse interpolation.

"Oh, sir—how I wish I were!" she whispered fervently, laying a hand impulsively on his sleeve. Heedless of his stare she rushed on breathlessly, "I had to come—not just to thank you on Kit's account but because you have been so very kind . . . " Swallowing hard, she extended a hand. "I wanted to speak with you before now but you have always been so much occupied and—and I thought if the ships arrive tomorrow I may not have the opportunity to say goodbye."

"My dear—" Moore pressed her into a chair and drew the candles nearer. "It has been a delight and a privilege to enjoy your society. Major Fane is a fortunate fellow," he added softly.

There followed a silence as though he were thinking deeply, then, "How do you happen to know of Miss Fox?"

Dindie flushed. "Captain Napier happened to mention that—that I resembled his cousin a little," she faltered.

"Ah." The general nodded absently.

In nervous apprehension Dindie waited, noting with an ache how worry and disappointment had prematurely lined and worn down the handsome features. When he still seemed sunk in reverie she rose awkwardly.

"I ought not to have intruded, sir."

"I am grateful that you have, Mrs Fane." Moore held her hand in a strong clasp and it seemed to Dindie that his air of sadness was momentarily dispelled.

"May you and your major always be happy," he murmured.

At the door Dindie asked in halting tones, "General—shall we get away in safety?"

"I suspect Marshall Soult means to bide his time until the moment of embarkation, when we shall be at our most vulnerable." The hazel eyes smiled ruefully. "That is what every good commander would choose. But I have a thrawn Scots streak in me, Mrs Fane. I do not see why we should not all be safely off within the next few days."

When she had gone Moore remained motionless, his eyes resolute and aglow. Caroline . . . she would be eighteen soon. A few months, he promised himself, and I shall go to her again with renewed hope.

15

BY NOON NEXT day Corunna Bay was crowded with high-masted men-of-war and a tingling expectancy pervaded the British camp. Moore's troops were already in position on the rough heights above the town and embarkation of the sick and wounded was going ahead.

Dindie removed the basin and towel from Kit's bedside and reached for the shirt which she had washed out the previous night, testing it against her cheek for signs of dampness before helping him into it. His fixed determination to attempt matters for himself was a heartening sign and each minor victory, even cleaning his teeth without exhaustion, was a milestone to be rejoiced over.

Yet when his strength failed to accomplish all he desired his frustration was acute. He raged at his own helplessness with fulsome oaths, denigrating himself in a manner that tore at Dindie's heart. It was not going to be easy for him to accept his disability; in many ways perhaps the hardest battle Kit would ever be called upon to fight. She knew it would require all the resources of her love and patience to sustain him through the struggle ahead. But he shall walk again, Dindie vowed. He shall!

She was become adept at cleaning his wound, and so light was her touch that he refused to suffer anyone else near. It still rendered stinking pus but she had persevered in her daily swabbing with boiled water and alcohol and the treatment seemed to be working, for healthy pink tissue was begun to appear at the outer edges of the stump.

Bathing him, however, was another matter. Kit absolutely

rebelled at her attempts, storming that it was no task for any woman, and most assuredly not for a lady.

Dindie retorted patiently that he need not suppose she might be put to the blush. Whom did he imagine had washed and changed him during the dark days of his fever when he was incontinent?

Kit stared at her thunderstruck. "You did all that?"

She turned rosy under his burning gaze. "It is no task to execute a disagreeable service for someone you love, Kit."

"Oh, Dindie," His face was a comic study.

Harry Percy stuck his sandy head round the door.

"The pinnace is waiting, Major. And the chief will want a word before you leave." To Dindie he asked, in an urgent undertone, "Shall I row out with you? You cannot hope to manage him alone."

She shook her head, touched by his consideration.

"No, Harry. You are needed here." Jamie would be waiting downstairs with Tom Jackson. Kit was not likely to welcome more fuss than was necessary.

*   *   *

Jamie unsaddled his mount for the last time and laid his head close to the roan's silken neck. He had kept delaying this moment, dreaded it with an irrational ache. Whisker emitted a low whinny and gazed at him through unblinking velvet eyes. A lump constricted Jamie's throat. He loved his old horse, owed his life to Whisker's endurance and fidelity throughout the harrowing weeks of retreat. But the sailors were showing signs of impatience. Hardening his heart he slapped the animal's haunches to send it away and climbed into the boat.

They were almost under the bows of the towering seventy-four when Dindie drew a sharp exclamation and pointed towards the shore. The roan had plunged into the sea after its master and was swimming behind the boat like a dog.

"No, Whisker, no!"

Near to tears, Jamie watched helplessly as the horse struggled valiantly to reach him, its terrified neighing carrying clearly as the waves rolled over its neck. Far better to have ended the animal's misery with a bullet before now, but Whisker was not broken-down and ailing like those wretched brutes on the beach. In desperation Jamie turned to the sailors pulling strongly on the oars. Hardened men that they were, even they could surely appreciate the trauma of his situation.

"Can't take him on board ship, sir," said one gruffly, after a momentary glance behind at the roan which was now only a short distance from the bobbing pinnace, its eyes rolling wildly against the spray from the boat's wash.

"There ain't no stalls for to put him in. I'm sorry. Real sorry."

Jamie nodded dumbly. He watched grim-faced as the sailors winched Kit aboard the man-of-war. It would never do to give way to the sharp prick of tears behind his eyes, not here in this open boat before these navy men.

A small hand slipped through his in a comforting squeeze.

"I'm sorry too, Jamie."

Watching him being torn apart with emotion it seemed to Dindie that all that was meaningful to him was being taken from him. He had come to Spain having lost the girl he hoped to marry, he must turn his back on the faithful creature which had been his close companion during the nightmare campaign, and he had lost her-self . . . or rather he must live with the knowledge that not even his love for her could compare with the merest caress from her husband's hand.

"Your turn now, lady."

Dindie cast a heartfelt glance at the young captain and prepared to join Kit aboard the battleship.

*　　　*　　　*

In the grey dawn of January 16th Sir John Moore was already out inspecting his forward outposts. To George Napier, watching the chief gallop energetically from one position to the next all along the line, he seemed like a man reborn. Moore's confidence in his Army remained absolute. Despite its grousing, its weakness for drink and its attempts at self-destruction he knew that at the first shot of battle every man would do his duty.

By ten o'clock there was still no sign of activity from the French-occupied ridge opposite. Moore rode back to Corunna leaving instructions that at the first sign of the enemy line getting under arms a signal of three guns should be fired.

He spent the remainder of the morning at headquarters issuing a last General Order and seeing some naval commanders and his quartermaster-general. Withdrawal would begin as soon as darkness fell. Everything was going ahead just as he had intended. His heart felt light. With luck he might be reunited at Brook Farm with his mother and sister before the space of a week.

George Napier rode in heated and grimy from a morning in the saddle to discover that the general and his staff had dined early in expectation of news from the front. Paul Anderson, Moore's assistant adjutant-general and closest friend, was being given a final briefing. Beside Sir John's commanding figure the wiry little colonel appeared dwarfed.

"Let there be as little confusion as possible." Moore glanced keenly round the bare room where papers and files had already been stacked in neat bundles by his military secretary. "Remember, men of the Reserve are to head the troop embarkation. Their exemplary conduct throughout merits first choice of berths — it is the least we can do to express gratitude."

Before Anderson had power to reply Colonel Thomas Graham burst in announcing breathlessly that he had just ridden from General Hope's position on the left of the line. The French had taken possession of a wood and had brought up four guns.

Moore was already striding towards the door.

"Napier, order the horses!"

They had just mounted when a sharp exclamation from Anderson died under the roar of gunfire. Another shot followed and a third. Battle was joined.

*   *   *

210

Below decks within the sick-bay of H.M.S. *Audacious* Dindie listened with Kit and Jamie to the triple signal. The ship lay-to outside the crescent-shaped harbour and the misty drizzle which hung perpetually over Corunna had lifted to reveal the rooftops and spires of the town clinging in tortuous gradients with the rise and fall of a music score.

Dindie screwed her eyes in an effort to identify the origins of the gunfire but nothing much could be distinguished astern save the Roman lighthouse known as the Tower of Hercules, which occupied a hill near the citadel.

She glanced towards Kit. He was staring fixedly through one of the gun-ports and she could tell by his eyes how much he longed to be participating in the action just begun. Even as they watched, swirling gunsmoke belched upwards from the twin ridges behind the town and a heavy barrage sent thunderous echoes across the expanse of sparkling water.

"*Tirailleurs.*" Jamie passed Kit the spy-glass which he had borrowed from one of the ship's officers. "Swarming down the slope — do you see?"

"What are *tirailleurs*?" whispered Dindie. Her throat was dry with apprehension. Kit's arm slipped round her waist, drawing her protectively close.

"Skirmishers, lovedy. The French equivalent of our riflemen — they are sent in first, giving protection to the columns of infantry until the charge is sounded." He offered her the spy-glass. "Come take a look. Not that much can be distinguished through the smoke."

Mutely Dindie shook her head. Beyond that obscuring veil husbands, brothers, sweethearts, fathers were engaged in a life and death struggle, dying in slow agony from hideous wounds . . . Her eyes filled at the futility of it, the wasted flowering of manhood in two great nations. Until now her romantic imagination had associated this corner of Spain with its place in English history. From this same harbour the Armada had sailed, great ships with gilded prows and long pennants flying. From Corunna Catherine of

Aragon had renounced family and homeland to marry Henry Tudor. John of Gaunt had landed here even earlier to lay claim to the throne of Castile. What part might this British Army play, she wondered, in the continuing cycle?

"They're nosing in with cavalry now! Damn their eyes, Jamie — if they succeed in turning the line it may cut off all hope of retreat to the harbour!"

"You can bet Soult will press our centre as hard as he dares," returned Jamie darkly. "There'll no' be muckle left standing of that wee hamlet in the middle."

"Its name is Elvina," said Dindie quietly. "George Napier told me his brother's regiment is positioned there."

*　　　*　　　*

The staccato rub-a-dub of the French *pas de charge* increased in volume over the cannonade's roar. Straining above the din in the rubble of Elvina to hear some remark addressed to him by his brigade commander, Major Charles Napier felt sorely the want of Moore's presence. All along their section of the line men of his regiment were dropping like flies under the murderous hail of enemy bullets that ricocheted from the lime-washed cottage walls and surrounding dykes. Yet another house was fallen to the advancing hordes. The British, though replying with vigour, were being relentlessly pushed back. As his men's stricken cries mingled with the devastating hiss and hum of shot and musket fire the cry went up, "Where is the general?"

And suddenly, as if alighting from the air, Sir John Moore was amongst them. So swiftly did he pull up that his foaming cream and black charger was thrown on its haunches, slithering to a terror-stricken halt with ears pushed forwards and nostrils distended. Moore was catapulted violently forwards almost to its neck but coolly kept control with his knees and a tight rein. Not once did his eyes waver from their fixed scrutiny of the advancing enemy column. Then without a word the general galloped on.

212

Spirits soared magically. Throughout the hard-pressed British line the feeling remained unshakeable that under Moore they could not be beaten. But the murderous fire increased and soon after his departure Elvina fell to the French.

Upon hearing the news the commander-in-chief immediately came spurring up, giving orders to George Napier to bring up the Guards in support. Seemingly devoid of exhaustion he exhibited the uncanny ability to be where he was most sorely needed when the situation demanded.

As he came galloping back in a dash of thrown-up dirt a French shell ripped the ground near by, tearing off the leg of a highlander of the Black Watch. The man screamed in agony and rolled to the ground, causing a gap in the ranks. Seeing the danger Moore signalled for him to be taken to the rear and addressed himself firmly to the highlander's shaken comrades.

"This is nothing, my lads. Keep your ranks." He bent from the saddle and spoke encouragingly to the writhing soldier.

"My good fellow, don't make such a noise — we must bear these things better."

Smoke hung heavy over the valley and the short winter's day was fast drawing to a close. The general's anxiety showed momentarily. His great fear was that darkness might close in before he had sufficiently pulverised the enemy to allow withdrawal and embarkation.

Galloping to the head of the 42nd Highlanders Moore ordered them to advance. Taking up his shout of "Remember Egypt!" the Black Watch emptied their muskets and charged, driving back the French to the foot of the hill.

George Napier watched his chief lead the kilted highlanders in their heroic charge. Seconds later, his brother Charles followed them with the 50th Regiment. He saw them check at a stone wall, then they were over with Charles swearing horribly at them to keep their aim low. Howitzers exploded from the hills and the sky was thick with pluming black smoke and shot.

Above the shrilling of bugles and the hoarse cries of "*En Avant!*

Tué! Tué!" from the enemy line, Moore's satisfied exclamation was heard by those nearest to him.

"Well done, 50th! Well done, my majors!"

But neither of his two majors heard the heartening shout. Charles Napier lay in the ruins of Elvina bleeding heavily from being run through by a French sword. And Lady Hester Stanhope's favourite brother Charles was already dead.

* * *

"Captain presents his compliments, Major Fane, and bids me report that your cabin is now ready."

Kit dragged himself into a sitting position with his elbows and stared hard at the naval lieutenant.

"Cabin? With a ship this full of military?" His brows contracted darkly. "You may thank Captain Gosselin for his generous offer — but I will not countenance priviliged treatment by the mere virtue of being on Sir John Moore's staff!"

The young naval officer looked uncomfortable.

"We were considering your lady, Major," he murmured, with a meaningful glance in Dindie's direction.

Kit read the burning entreaty in his wife's eyes. Two bright spots of colour mantled her cheeks, and a soft curl of ripe brown hair had escaped from its upswept coil and lay tantalisingly on the warm smoothness of her neck.

"Very well," said Kit softly. "If the captain insists."

There was more than one good reason why the privacy of a cabin shared with his young wife should all at once become desirable.

When the lieutenant had departed Dindie nestled close and slipped both her hands in his, whispering tremulously, "You need not have sacrificed your principles on my account, Kit."

"I didn't." There was a lurking and extremely reprehensible twinkle in his grey eyes, that caused Dindie to turn rosy. Turning up her mouth he kissed her with a tender thoroughness, exhibiting total unconcern for the riveted interest of the crowded cots of

214

wounded soldiery around them, and raised her palm softly to his cheek.

A warm sweetness filled Dindie's mind. She wanted his kiss to last for ever and when she felt his body tense fractionally she opened her eyes with reluctance, sighing to recapture the delight of his mouth on hers.

"I thought you had taken to wearing your wedding-ring again," said Kit slowly, examining her fingers.

"But I have . . . " Dindie stared in consternation at her naked hand. "Dear God, I — I must have lost it!" Sudden tears stung her vision and she dropped to her knees in a frenzy of searching. "I must find it! I must, Kit . . . "

"You had it on your finger this morning when you were about to change my bandages. Is it possible you may have — "

"Yes, oh yes! I removed my ring before bathing your wound!"

Scrambling to her feet she ran to the stairway, almost colliding with Jamie who had gone on deck to witness better the battle's progress. Dindie blurted out her tragic news, feeling her heart hammer painfully against her ribs. What if her precious ring was no longer in their room at headquarters? What if . . .

"The pinnace! It will be returning to shore for more sick — "

"*No, Dindie*! I absolutely forbid you to go back! Why, the French may shell the town any second. For God's sake, Jamie, stop her!" Cursing furiously at his own helplessness, Kit strove to grasp at her arm.

"Kit, I *must* search for it! Don't you understand? It is my wedding-ring . . . you gave it me, Kit." She was almost weeping.

"My heart's darling, I shall buy you another." In a terse voice he whispered, "You know what the French do to women."

Only Dindie knew what it cost him to voice such a fear. Her limbs turned to water at the prospect of returning to shore but the piercing intensity of her loss forced her to choke down her terror. She knew she had to return. "Another wedding-ring could never be the same . . . I — I shall ask Tom Jackson to accompany me." Her eyes burned into his. "I beg you, Kit!"

"Never mind Jackson." Jamie's tone of quiet finality cut through her plea. "I'm going back with you." He turned to Kit, "The action is still concentrated on the heights. If we hurry, we ought to return safely within the hour."

"Will you?" Kit stared fixedly at his young wife, his eyes bleak with a new desolation that took some minutes for her to interpret, and the realisation when it struck tore her heart. He believes I will run off with Jamie, that the whole business is pre-arranged, she thought chokily. Oh, Kit . . .

There was no time to spare for reassurance. Wrenching her gaze free, Dindie ran after Jamie, not daring to glance back.

*　　　*　　　*

George Napier took a last look over the smoking hell of gutted houses and shell-blasted orchards which had been Elvina. The winter sun dazzled his eyes as it slipped in a final blaze behind the darkening hills. His scarlet uniform was caked with mud but he himself had mercifully come through unscathed. He tried not to think of the many friends he had lost in this afternoon's work.

Behind him at the cross-roads Sir John Moore was reined in with Colonel Graham and young Percy when Henry Hardinge came galloping up to report. Napier saw his brother aide's horse draw almost abreast of the general when a cannon ball hurled Moore from the saddle.

He was flung on his back at Graham's feet, a look of surprise still on his face. George's heart almost stopped. The others had leaped from their horses to support the chief and every instinct prompted him to join them. He knew Moore must be wounded but duty reminded him that the chief had entrusted him with vital orders to bring up the Guards. Sick at heart Napier galloped furiously off on his mission.

Thomas Graham knelt quickly, relieved to see no apparent injury. Then as Moore struggled to raise himself they saw the mess of blood spurting through his uniform. His left shoulder had been shot away.

216

He was lifted gently to the shelter of a bank and a medical officer was urgently summoned. Whilst he waited, the general continued to look about him at the battle's progress. He made no murmur but he held fast to Hardinge's hand.

"The 42nd are advancing, sir." Choking back tears young Hardinge made feverish attempts to staunch the terrible gush of blood with his waist-sash. Christ God, where was the M.O.? Relief swept over him as a surgeon of the Royals came hurrying up.

The man took one look at the general's wound and muttered, "Hopeless."

The left arm remained attached by strips of skin only, the shoulder itself completely shattered, gouging a hole so deep that the lung lay exposed. The rib-cage was smashed and protruding horribly, and a piece of thick uniform lapel with two buttons still attached had been driven deep into the pulsing remains.

Very gently the surgeon extracted the piece of cloth from the wound. Moore thanked him but shook his head.

"My good man," he whispered. "You can do me no good. It is too high up," He turned his head and looked steadfastly at his gaping chest for some seconds, then consented to be taken to the rear.

Six men from the Black Watch and Guards transferred him carefully into a blanket slung between two poles and the little procession wound slowly from the smoke-hung battlefield, with Moore's grieving staff officers taking up the rear. As sunset gilded the distant spires and windows of Corunna and the sound of gunfire receded behind them Moore frequently made his bearers stop so that he might view the battle's progress. Word had been brought that Sir David Baird had been badly hit and his arm amputated. Moore immediately ordered Hardinge to report to General Hope, who must now take command.

"Sir . . . I had rather stay with you." The aide-de-camp's face crumpled unashamedly. His crimson sash which he had slipped under the chief to support him in an easy posture was already sodden with blood. Moore's finely-wrought sword of East India workmanship had pierced his wound as they lifted him into the stretcher but like a Spartan his shield, the general had refused to be parted from it, declaring resolutely, "I had rather it should go out of the field with me."

*   *   *

Screeching bullock carts laden with ammunition on their way to the front passed in endless procession as Dindie hurried with a palpitating heart towards the headquarters house, on Jamie's arm. The trees on the Canton Grande were tossing wildly under a strong wind and the terrible thunder of the guns from the neighbouring heights carried clearly, bringing a chill reminder of their peril.

"Jamie," she began hesitantly, "you — you do not detest me for electing to remain with Kit?" It was out, the pent-up question that she knew must be settled between them before she could be truly happy in her husband's love.

Jamie stared fixedly before him, walking with long purposeful strides. "Nothing you do could ever make me detest you, Dindie. I knew within myself that my cause was hopeless."

"Oh, Jamie." Her eyes filled suddenly. "You will never know just how greatly your support and — and regard have carried me through these past weeks." She faced him squarely, laying one hand impulsively on his sleeve. "Despite what you believe at this moment, you will find someone whose love will make you happy as you deserve — much, much happier than ever you would be with me."

At that he smiled faintly and drew her to a railing which over-looked the crowded harbour. "You cannot expect me to forget you, my dear — and I don't know that I can promise to be happy without you but," his mouth twisted wryly, "I shall want to be a godparent when you and Kit christen your first bairn."

Her breath escaped in a long sigh. "Oh, how I wish you may be proved right. I want Kit's baby more than anything."

Jamie stared resolutely out to sea. "You'll have a big family of brown-eyed bairns, Dindie, never fear." Then, in a tight voice, "We had best hasten to find your ring."

218

To their surprise a jam-packed crowd of British and Spanish officers was formed round the entrance to Moore's balconied headquarters. As Dindie and her tall escort approached, a chaplain pushed through and was admitted and all eyes turned instinctively to the windows on the first floor.

A premonition gripped Dindie's insides. Without pausing to ask questions she squirmed a path to the entrance hall and darted up the familiar staircase, sickly fear churning her stomach at what she might find.

In the darkened writing-room bare of all equipment and personal belongings Sir John Moore lay on a mattress on the floor, surrounded by a stunned and grieving knot of staff officers. Dindie clung to the door handle, swaying a little as her horror-stricken gaze took in the mortal nature of his wound. As her eyes became accustomed to the gloom she recognised Harry Percy standing alone before the window and made her way to his side, whispering chokily, "Is — is there no hope?"

Percy turned a broken-hearted face to hers and shook his head, too overcome with grief to reply. In silence Dindie watched Colonel Anderson kneel by his friend's side, pillowing the general's head with his one good arm. Moore's eyes were bright but every breath was an agony to him and he was slipping into incoherence, muttering half-finished sentences only to stir in agitation as some new thought occurred to him.

The surgeons made to come near but the little colonel waved them fiercely back. They had already been working at the wound but everyone could see that it was useless, that their efforts must only cause unnecessary agony. Moore knew it also. In the darkness he felt for Paul Anderson's hand and gripped it fast, whispering, "Anderson — don't leave me."

Tears poured down Anderson's face as he murmured reassurance. Presently the general said, in a stronger voice, "You know, I have always wished to die this way."

Another spasm gripped him but his face remained calm and only its deathly pallor hinted at the terrible pain he suffered.

219

Dindie subsided to the floor, staring dry-eyed before her. All thoughts of her original mission was forgotten. Nothing would make her quit this room while there remained the least flutter of life in that well-loved frame. The general had come to mean much to her in a way that had nothing to do with the deeply passionate love she felt for Kit. Their lives had touched briefly. Between them was the spontaneous understanding of kindred spirits, an unspoken recognition of the other's loneliness. She had reminded him, be it ever so lightly, of his own cherished love . . . Dindie wanted to stroke his hand, comfort him in this darkest hour, but grief held her rooted. She could only remain on her knees on the perimeter of the hushed group with tears pressing upwards in her throat and the knowledge that with every second Moore's life was ebbing away.

Officers of his staff tiptoed into the room, their faces stunned and disbelieving. To each he addressed the urgent question, "Are the French beaten?"

His voice was growing hoarse from inward bleeding and as his wound congealed and the agony doubled he sought refuge in long silences, fighting his inward battle to bear the pain with composure.

"I hope the people of England will be satisfied . . . Anderson, say to my mother . . . " His voice failed in anguish. Then, hoarsely, "Are Colonel Graham and all my aides well?"

No one dared break the news that little Harry Burrard was dangerously wounded. Satisfied, Moore fell back weakly on the pillow. "Colborne has my will — and all my papers."

Colborne himself entered the room at that moment and Sir John, as though struggling to summon the last vestiges of strength left to him, fastened his eyes on the blanched face of his military secretary. "The French," he whispered, "Are they beat?"

"In every point, sir," replied Colborne, close to tears.

"Well, it is a great satisfaction to me."

His bright gaze rested upon the little group of officers gathered in anguished silence about the empty room. Graham, grave but resolute, Colborne kneeling next to Anderson with his face beneath its streaks of dirt white as the powder stains on his uniform, curly-haired Harry Percy manfully choking down his grief. Dindie's heart pounded as the hazel eyes fixed upon her intently. Drawn by the heart-rending expression, more eloquent than any words, she came and knelt beside him, cradling his cold hand gently in both her own, hardly able to see for a sudden misting of tears.

She had no way of knowing whether he recognised her for herself, or if he fancied himself in the presence of that other, dearer being. She felt his gaze rest contentedly upon her face for some minutes, then almost apologetically he shook his head, whispering softly to her, "I feel myself so strong. I fear I shall be a long time dying."

*   *   *

George Napier rode into Corunna like a man possessed. In just a few short hours his world had fallen apart. The general whom he revered as a father was wounded, mortally some said. His brother Charles was reported dead and he had returned to Elvina accompanied by young James Stanhope, turning over every officer's corpse in a frenzy of grief. The handsome, marbled features of Major Stanhope were an early discovery but of his own brother's body there was no sign and when James had composed himself they set spurs for Sir John Moore's headquarters.

A chill silence hung about the house as George Napier bounded up the stairs. No lights burned in any front window. As he reached a bend in the stairs a shattering report from Admiral Hood's flagship in the harbour signalled eight o'clock, and as its echoes died away another sound turned his blood cold, that of a man weeping uncontrollably.

Bursting into the room George knew instinctively that he was come too late. Young Harry Percy was sobbing his heart out and James Stanhope who had entered the room minutes before had also broken down. Sir John Moore lay in death, the well-loved features tranquil and his hand clasped in that of Colonel Anderson. At his other side crouched in an agony of grief George recognised the wife of Major Fane.

Napier crept from the scene and sat himself heavily on the stairs alongside the young cavalry officer whom he had scarcely noticed in his headlong dash to the first floor. Too grief-stricken to weep, he could only stare at his hands. Moore was gone. And he had not been at his general's side at the last.

Daylight was growing as Moore's tall frame was carried to his last resting-place still in the familiar scarlet and gold uniform, and shrouded in a rough blanket with his military cloak gently draped over it. There was no time for a coffin to be prepared, for the French bombardment of the rescue fleet was already begun. A gale blew strongly billowing the white clerical bands and black cassock of the young chaplain as he faltered over the final prayer. Only four staff officers bore their general to the landward bastion of the citadel overlooking Corunna — Colonel Paul Anderson, Moore's faithful military secretary, white-lipped and near to breaking down, and two of his aides-de-camp, Harry Percy and James Stanhope, the latter treasuring the general's dying whisper, "Remember me to your sister."

With military precision they stepped forward as one and with their long crimson silk sashes lowered the body of their beloved commander-in-chief into the shallow grave. The wind buffeted keenly into their faces as they straightened. It was just turned eight o'clock on a cold January morning.

*   *   *

In the privacy of their cabin aboard H.M.S. *Audacious* Dindie raised her head from Kit's shoulder and gazed at the receding horizon. With every minute the white wake of the ship lengthened, bearing them ever closer to England and home.

She felt his arm tighten about her. Pressing close, she lifted her tear-stained face in anticipation of his kiss.

"He wanted us to be happy, Kit," she whispered chokily.

"We shall be," he returned softly, caressing the gold band that gleamed once more upon her third finger. "I'm glad that one of us was present, Dindie — I only wish to Heaven it had been myself."

On deck George Napier heard the splash as the shrouded body of little Burrard was consigned to the grey deep. Another death, yet another gone to whom he had grown close. He could not know that his beloved elder brother Charles, though gravely wounded, was at that moment a prisoner of the French. Burying his dark head against his sleeve Napier burst unashamedly into tears.

Kit also heard the splash and recognised it for what it was. Before Dindie might question its source he pulled her swiftly down against the pillows and planted his mouth on hers. Never had she appeared more enchanting with her hair all tousled and her brown eyes still heavy with sleep.

His kiss awoke in Dindie a flame of physical longing so consuming in its urgency that her heart soared in an ecstasy of joy. His love had broken the spell, released her from the fear which had threatened to destroy their marriage.

"Oh, Dindie . . . so many wasted months."

"Not wasted, Kit. I — I was not ready to be a wife to you before."

"And are you ready now, wifeling?" he whispered.

Dindie looked shyly into her husband's eyes and read the unspoken question, the desperate uncertainty behind his tenderness. This was not the fanciful Launcelot of her girlhood but a fallible man possessed of frailties and shortcomings, a human being with ordinary needs and desires. And because he was less than perfect her love for him burned the more strongly.

With a deep sigh as though ridding herself of a leaden burden she replied simply, "Yes — oh yes, Kit. I'm ready."

Behind them orange and pink clouds peeped over the Spanish coastline as the great flotilla of transports turned into the wind. And on the ramparts of Corunna the smoke of battle hung like a light pall over a freshly dug grave.

223